MW00439462

ESSENTIAL
GERMAN
DICTIONARY

Kate Needham

Illustrated by Ann Johns

Designed by Kathy Ward

Language consultants:
Sandy Walker & Anke Kornmüller

Series editor: Nicole Irving
Series designer: Amanda Barlow

CONTENTS

Further assistance from
Rachel Bladon & Sybille Frase

About this dictionary

This dictionary gives you all the up-to-date German words you need to get around Germany: words to help you find your way, book a place to stay, get a meal, buy a drink or take part in a sport.

It is a list of essential words. If the word you want is missing, think of one you could use instead.

A typical entry in the English to German list looks like this:

```
                    ┌──────── This is the word you looked up.
           ┌──────── This is the German translation.
pink rosa rawzah ────────┐
           This is the German pronunciation hint.
           Read it as if it were an English word,
           stressing the part that is underlined.
           (For more on pronunciation, see p. 45.)
```

Here are a few other points to bear in mind:

ß is a German letter that is sometimes used instead of "ss". It sounds just like "ss".

OR introduces an extra German translation. Words in brackets after OR hint at the difference in meaning:

fat (on meat) **das Fett** *fet*, OR (large) **dick** *dik*

der/die/das All German nouns[1] have a gender: they are masculine, feminine or neuter. So that you know which gender each noun is, they are listed with the German for "the" - **der** for masculine, **die** for feminine and **das** for neuter.

(n) (se) (-) To form the plural (more than one), German nouns usually add various letters. These are shown in brackets at the end of the word. **(-)** means that a word does not change in the plural:

```
                Don't add anything for the
                plural: Zimmer (rooms).
                   │
room das Zimmer(-) tsimmer
bus der Bus(se) booss(a)
                   │
                └── Add these letters for the
                    plural: Busse (buses).
```

⸚ is called an umlaut. It goes over an "a", "o" or "u" and changes its sound slightly. In the plural, many nouns add ⸚ to the last "a", "o" or "u" (or to "a" if the last two vowels are "au"):

In the English to German list (p. 4-43), illustrations with labels provide lots of extra words. If you are ever unsure of their meaning, look them up in the German to English list (p. 46-64).

Below are some tips about using this dictionary. Newcomers to German should also see **Getting by in German** (p. 44-45).

bike *das Fahrrad(¨er) farraht* PL: *farraider*
```
                In the plural, put ¨ over the last a,
                and add er: Fahrräder (bikes).
```
PL: introduces an unusual plural and/or an unusual plural pronunciation:

hand *die Hand(¨e) hunt* PL: *henda*

[m] [f] [n] A few words are usually used without **der**, **die** or **das**. So that you know their gender, they are followed by [m] for masculine, [f] for feminine and [n] for neuter:

Britain Großbritannien [n] *grawssbritunnyen*

[pl] The word for "the" in the plural is **die**, the same as in the feminine. Words which are given in the plural are followed by [pl]:

news *die Nachrichten* [pl] *nukh-rikhten*

[+ acc] [+ dat] German has a system of cases[2]. Some words are always followed by the same case. [+ acc] shows a word that takes the accusative case; [+ dat] shows one that takes the dative.

~ follows parts of words that you attach to the beginning of a noun:

double Doppel~ *doppel* E.G. double bed **das Doppelbett**

* indicates words that are familiar or slangy, and that may be too casual if used in the wrong situation. Use them with friends of your own age, but avoid them in formal situations.

' some German verbs[1] are separable, (see p. 45). ' indicates where they separate:

to arrive an'kommen *un-kommen*

Verbs are listed in the infinitive form. This means they are preceded by "to", e.g. "to eat", "to walk", but you will find them listed under "e" for "eat", "w" for "walk", etc.

[1]: For more about nouns and verbs, see p. 44-45. [2]: For more about cases, see p. 44.

Absolute essentials

Here are some useful, ready-made phrases you may need:

I'd like ...
Ich möchte ...
ikh _murkh_ta ...

Could I have ...?
Ich hätte gern ...
ikh _hetta_ gairn ...

Where is ...?
Wo ist ...?
vaw isst ...

What's this?
Was ist das?
vuss isst _duss_

I don't understand.
Ich verstehe nicht.
ikh fair-_shtaya_ nikht

Leave me alone!
Laß mich in Ruhe!
luss mikh in _roo_-a

How much is this?
Wieviel kostet das?
veefeel _kos_tet duss

I'm very sorry.
Es tut mir sehr leid
ess _toot_ meer zair _lyte_

Do you speak English?
Sprechen Sie Englisch?
_shprekh_en zee eng-lish

A little slower, please.
Ein bißchen langsamer, bitte.
ine _biss_-khen _lung_zum-er bitta

Could you write it down for me?
Könnten Sie es mir aufschreiben?
_kurn_ten zee ess meer _aowf_-shrye-ben

What's that called in German?
Wie heißt das auf deutsch?
vee _hye-sst_ duss owf _doytsh_

Can you say that again, please?
Wie war das noch 'mal, bitte?
vee var duss _nokh_ _mahl_ bitta

Could you tell me where the toilet is?
Wo sind die Toiletten, bitte?
vaw zint dee twu-_letten_ bitta

Numbers

0 *null* _nooll_
1 *eins* _ine_-s
2 *zwei* _tsvye_
3 *drei* _dry_
4 *vier* _feer_
5 *fünf* _foonf_
6 *sechs* _zex_
7 *sieben* _zeeben_
8 *acht* _ukht_
9 *neun* _noyn_
10 *zehn* _tsain_
11 *elf* _elf_
12 *zwölf* _tsvurlf_
13 *dreizehn* _dry_-tsain
14 *vierzehn* _feer_-tsain
15 *fünfzehn* _foonf_-tsain
16 *sechzehn* _sekh_-tsain
17 *siebzehn* _zeep_-tsain
18 *achtzehn* _ukh_-tsain
19 *neunzehn* _noyn_-tsain
20 *zwanzig* _tsvun_-tsikh
21 *einundzwanzig* ine-oont-_tsvun_-tsikh
22 *zweiundzwanzig* tsvye-oont-_tsvun_-tsikh
30 *dreißig* _dry_-ssikh
40 *vierzig* _feer_-tsikh
50 *fünfzig* _foonf_-tsikh
60 *sechzig* _sekh_-tsikh
70 *siebzig* _zeep_-tsikh
80 *achtzig* _ukh_-tsikh
90 *neunzig* _noyn_-tsikh
100 *hundert* _hoon_dert
101 *hunderteins* _hoon_dert-_ine_-s
102 *hundertzwei* _hoon_dert-_tsvye_
200 *zweihundert* tsvye-_hoon_dert
210 *zweihundertzehn* tsvye-_hoon_dert-_tsain_
300 *dreihundert* _dry_-_hoon_-dert
1 000 *tausend* _taow_zent
1 100 *tausendeinhundert* _taow_zent-ine-_hoon_dert
1 200 *tausendzweihundert* _taow_zent-tsvye-_hoon_dert
2 000 *zweitausend* _tsvye_-taowzent
10 000 *zehntausend* _tsain_-taowzent
100 000 *hunderttausend* _hoon_dert-taowzent
1 000 000 *eine Million* _ine_-a mill_yawn_
2 000 000 *zwei Millionen* tsvye mill_yawnen_

3

a, an *ein* [m, n] _ine_, OR *eine* [f] _ine-a_ (These words change in different cases, see p. 44)
about (approximately) *ungefähr* oongefair; what's it about? (film, book) *worum geht es?* vawroom gate ess
above (higher than) *über* [+ acc or dat][1] _oohber_, OR (overhead) *oben* _awben_

Ich habe Kopfschmerzen.
ikh hahba kopf-shmairtsen

to ache Schmerzen haben

Ich habe Zahnschmerzen.
ikh hahba tsahn-shmairtsen

Ich habe Ohrenschmerzen.
ich hahba awren-shmairtsen

Ich habe Bauchschmerzen.
ikh hahba baowkh-shmairtsen

Ich habe Rückenschmerzen.
ikh hahba rooken-shmairtsen

abroad (to be abroad) *im Ausland* im _owss-lunt_, OR (to go abroad) *ins Ausland* inz _owss-lunt_
accent *der Akzent(e)* aktsent(a)
to accept *akzeptieren* aktsepteeren, OR (an offer) *an'nehmen* _un-naymen_
accident *der Unfall(¨e)* _oonful_ PL: _oonfella_
accommodation (places to stay) *die Unterkunft* _oonter-koonft_
to ache (or to have a head/back etc. ache) *Schmerzen haben* shmairtsen _hahben_ (See pictures on this page)
to act (theatre) *spielen* shpeelen
actor *der Schauspieler(-)* shaow-shpeeler
actress *die Schauspielerin(nen)* shaow-shpeelerin(en)
to add *hinzu'fügen* hintsoo-foohgen
address *die Adresse(n)* udressa(n)
adopted *adoptiert* udopteert
adult *der/die Erwachsene(n)* airvuxana(n)
advantage *der Vorteil(e)* for-tyle(-a); to take advantage of *aus'nutzen* [+ acc] owssnootsen
adventurous (person) *abenteuerlustig* ahbentoyer-loosstikh, OR (journey) *abenteuerlich* ahbentoyer-likh
advertisement (in paper) *die Anzeige(n)* un-tsye-ga(n), OR (at cinema, on TV) *die Werbung(en)* vairboong(en); classified ads *die Annoncen* unnonssen
advice *der Rat* raht
aerobics *das Aerobic* airobik
after *nach* [+ dat] nukh
afternoon *der Nachmittag(e)* nukhmittahg(a)
afterwards *nachher* nukh-hair
again *wieder* veeder, OR *noch mal** nokh mahl
against *gegen* [+ acc] gaigen
age *das Alter(-)* ulter; under age *minderjährig* minder-yairikh
ago *vor* [+ dat] for, E.G. a week ago *vor einer Woche*
to agree *einverstanden sein* ine-fair-shtunden zyne
aid *die Hilfe* hilfa
AIDS *AIDS* aids
air *die Luft* looft; in the open air *im Freien* im fryen; air-conditioned *klimatisiert* kleemahteezeert; air stewardess *die Stewardeß* shtooardess(en) PL: *Stewardessen*
airline *die Fluggesellschaft(en)* floog-gazellshufft(en)
airmail *Luftpost* looftposst
airport *der Flughafen(¨)* floog-hahfen PL: _flooghayfen_
alarm clock *der Wecker(-)* vekker

4 1: If your sentence involves movement, use the accusative case; if not, use the dative. For more about cases, see p. 44. 2: If you are talking about a female, add *in* (*innen* in the plural).

album *das Album* <u>u</u>lboom PL: *Alben* <u>u</u>lben

alcohol *der Alkohol* <u>u</u>lkawhawl

alcoholic (drink) *alkoholisch* ulkawh<u>aw</u>lish

all *alle* <u>u</u>lla, OR (whole) *ganz* <u>gu</u>nts; all day *den ganzen Tag* dain g<u>u</u>ntsen tahg; all of it *alles* <u>u</u>lless; all right (I agree) *in Ordnung* in <u>o</u>rdnoong, OR (it's OK) *es geht* ess g<u>a</u>yt

allergy *die Allergie(n)* ulair<u>ghee</u>(yen)

alone *allein* ull<u>y</u>ne

already *schon* <u>shaw</u>n

also *auch* <u>aow</u>kh

always *immer* <u>imm</u>er

amazing (unbelievable) *unglaublich* oongl<u>aow</u>blikh, OR (astonishing) *erstaunlich* airsht<u>aow</u>nlikh, OR (fabulous) *toll** tol

ambulance *der Krankenwagen(-)* kr<u>u</u>nken-vahgen

America *Amerika* [n] ah-m<u>airee</u>kah

American *amerikanisch* umairee<u>kah</u>nish, OR (man) *Amerikaner(-)* umairee<u>kah</u>ner, OR (woman) *Amerikanerin(nen)* umairee<u>kah</u>nerin(nen)

and *und* <u>oo</u>nt

angry *böse* <u>bur</u>za, OR *verärgert* fair-<u>airg</u>urt

animal *das Tier(e)* <u>teer</u>(a)

ankle *das Fußgelenk(e)* <u>fooss</u>-galenk(a)

to annoy *ärgern* <u>airg</u>urn; to be/get annoyed *sich ärgern* zikh <u>airg</u>urn

annoying *lästig* <u>les</u>tikh, OR (very) *ärgerlich* <u>airg</u>urlikh

answer *die Antwort(en)* <u>u</u>ntvort(en)

to answer (someone) *antworten* [+ dat] <u>u</u>ntvorten, OR (question) *beantworten* ba-<u>u</u>ntvorten, OR (phone) *ran'gehen** r<u>u</u>n-gayen, OR (door) *hin'gehen* <u>hin</u>-gayen

answering machine *der Anrufbeantworter(-)* <u>u</u>nroofba-<u>u</u>ntvorter

antibiotic *das Antibiotikum* unteebee-<u>aw</u>teekoom PL: *Antibiotika* unteebee-<u>aw</u>teekah

antiseptic *antiseptisch* unte<u>es</u>eptish

any (See not any)

anyone (as in "is anyone there?") *jemand* <u>yay</u>munt, OR (stressed, as in "is <u>anyone</u> there?") *irgend jemand* <u>ee</u>rgunt <u>yay</u>munt, OR (any old person, as in "anyone will do") *jeder* <u>yay</u>ider F: *jede* <u>yay</u>ida (See also nobody)

anything (as in "do you like anything?") *etwas* <u>e</u>tvuss, OR (stressed, as in "do you like <u>anything</u>?") *irgend etwas* <u>ee</u>rgunt <u>e</u>tvuss (See also nothing)

anywhere *irgendwo* <u>ee</u>rguntvaw, OR (no matter where) *egal wo* ayg<u>ah</u>l vaw (See also nowhere)

apple *der Apfel(¨)* <u>u</u>pfel PL: <u>e</u>pfel (See also picture right)

3: *Schmerztablette* means "painkiller". This is what you ask for in German if you need an aspirin.

appointment *die Verabredung(en)* fair-<u>u</u>praidoong(en), OR (with doctor, lawyer) *der Termin(e)* tairm<u>een</u>(a)

apricot *die Aprikose(n)* up-ree<u>kaw</u>za(n)

April *April* [m] <u>u</u>prill

arcade (amusement) *die Spielhalle(n)* shp<u>ee</u>lhulla(n)

area (region) *die Gegend(en)* g<u>ai</u>gunt PL: g<u>ai</u>gunden, OR (in town) *das Viertel(-)* f<u>ee</u>rtel

argument *die Auseinandersetzung(en)* aowss-eye-n<u>a</u>nderzetsoong(en), OR (quarrel) *der Streit(e)* sht<u>ryt</u>e(-a); to have an argument *sich streiten* zikh sht<u>ry</u>te-en

arm *der Arm(e)* <u>arm</u>(a)

to arrive *an'kommen* <u>u</u>n-kommen

art *die Kunst* <u>koonst</u>; art school *die Kunsthochschule(n)* <u>koonst</u>-hawkhshoola(n)

artist *der Künstler(-)²* <u>koon</u>stler

as (like) *wie* <u>vee</u>; (just) as... as *(genau)so... wie* (<u>genaow</u>)-zaw... vee; as usual *wie üblich* <u>vee</u> <u>ooh</u>blikh

ashtray *der Aschenbecher(-)* <u>u</u>shenbekher

to ask *fragen* fr<u>ah</u>gen; to ask a question *eine Frage stellen* ine-a fr<u>ah</u>ga shtellen; to ask out *ein'laden* <u>ine</u>-lahden

aspirin *die Schmerztablette(n)³* shm<u>airts</u>tubletta(n)

assistant (in shop, store) *der Verkäufer(-)²* fair<u>koy</u>fer

asthma *das Asthma* <u>us</u>tma

at (time) *um* <u>oom</u>, OR (place, as in "at the bus stop/corner") *an* [+ dat] <u>un</u>, OR (place, as in "at the bank/school") *auf* [+ dat] <u>aowf</u>, OR (as in "at Anna's") *bei* [+ dat] by

attractive *reizvoll* <u>rits</u>-foll, OR *attraktiv* utruk<u>teef</u>

audience *das Publikum* p<u>oo</u>blikoom

August *August* [m] aow-g<u>oost</u>

Australia *Australien* [n] aow-str<u>ah</u>leeyen

Australian *australisch* aow-str<u>ah</u>lish, OR (man) *Australier(-)* aow-str<u>ah</u>leeyer, OR (woman) *Australierin(nen)* aow-str<u>ah</u>leeyerin(nen)

apple *der Apfel*

die Schale <u>shah</u>la

das Kerngehäuse <u>kairn</u>-gehoyza

der Kern <u>kairn</u>

der Stiel <u>shteel</u>

Austria Österreich [n] _urster-eye-kh_
Austrian österreichisch _urster-eye-khish_, OR
(man) **Österreicher(-)** _urster-eye-kher_, OR (woman)
Österreicherin(nen) _urster-eye-kherin(nen)_
author der Autor(en)¹ _aow-tor(en)_
autumn der Herbst(e) _hairpst(a)_
avalanche die Lawine(n) _luveena(n)_
average durchschnittlich _doorkh_-shnittlikh,
OR (neither good nor bad) **mittelmäßig**
mittelmaissikh
avocado die Avocado(s) _uvawkahdaw(s)_
to avoid vermeiden _fair-my-den_
away weg _vaig_
awful furchtbar _foorkhtbar_

back (part of body) der Rücken(-) _rooken_, OR
(as in "go/come back") **zurück** _tsoorook_, OR (not
front) **die Hinterseite(n)** _hinter-zyta(n)_
backpack der Rucksack("e) _rookzuk_
PL: _rookzekka_
bad schlecht _shlekht_, OR **schlimm** _shlim_, OR
(naughty) **böse** _burza_; too bad! **Pech!** _pekh_
badge (metal) der Anstecker(-) _unshtekker_, OR
(stick on) **der Aufkleber(-)** _aowf-klaiber_
badminton Federball [m] _fayderbul_, OR
Badminton [n] _betminten_
bag die Tasche(n) _tusha(n)_
baker's die Bäckerei(en) _bekka-rye(-n)_
balcony der Balkon(s) _bulkon(s)_, OR (in
theatre) **oberster Rang** [m] _awbester rung_
ball der Ball("e) _bul_ PL: _bella_
ballet das Ballett _bulett_
banana die Banane(n) _bunahna(n)_
band (musical) die Band(s) _bend(s)_ (See also
picture right)
Band-aid® das Pflaster(-) _pfluster_
bank (money) die Bank(en) _bunk(en)_
bar die Bar(s) _bahr(s)_, OR (counter) **die
Theke(n)** _taika(n)_
bargain: it's a bargain **das ist (aber)
günstig** _duss_ isst _(ahber)_ _goonstikh_
baseball Baseball [m] _bazebul_
basketball Basketball [m] _busketbul_
bat (sport) der Schläger(-) _shlaiger_
bath das Bad("er) _baht_ PL: _baider_, OR (bath tub)
die Badewanne(n) _bahdevunna(n)_
bathroom das Badezimmer(-) _bahdetsimmer_
battery die Batterie(n) _buttairee(yen)_
to be sein _zyne_ (See also Verbs, p. 45), OR (as
in "to be right/hungry") **haben** _hahben_
beach der Strand("e) _shtrunt_ PL: _shtrenda_
bean die Bohne(n) _bawna(n)_
beard der Bart("e) _bart_ PL: _bairta_
beautiful schön _shurn_

because weil _vile_; because of **wegen** [+ dat]
vaigen
bed das Bett(en) _bet(en)_; double bed **das
Doppelbett(en)** _doppel-bet(en)_
bedroom das Schlafzimmer(-) _shlahftsimmer_
beef das Rindfleisch _rintfly-sh_
beer das Bier(e)² _beer(a)_, OR (on tap) **das
Faßbier(e)²** _fussbeer(a)_
beetle (insect or VW car) der Käfer(-) _kaifer_
before vor [+ dat] _for_, OR (followed by a
clause, as in "look before you go") **bevor** _befor_,
OR (beforehand) **vorher** _for-hair_
beggar der Bettler(-)¹ _betler_
beginner der Anfänger(-)¹ _unfenger_
beginning der Anfang("e) _unfung_ PL: _unfeng-a_
behind hinter [+ acc or dat]³ _hinter_, OR (at
the back) **hinten** _hinten_
belt der Gürtel(-) _goohrtle_
bend (in the road) die Kurve(n) _koorva(n)_
best (person or thing, as in "the best film")
beste(n) _besta(n)_, OR (action, as in "Peter plays
best") **am besten** um _besten_, OR (most of all, as
in "I like tennis best") **am liebsten** um _leepsten_
better besser _besser_
between zwischen [+ acc or dat]³ _tsvishen_
big groß _grawss_
bike das Fahrrad("er) _farraht_ PL: _farraider_, OR
das Rad("er) _raht_ PL: _raider_; racing bike **das
Rennrad("er)** _renraht_ PL: _renraider_; mountain
bike **das Mountainbike(s)** (See also
motorbike and picture opposite)

band die Band

Schlagzeug [n]
shlahg-tsoyg

die Gitarristin **die Gitarre**
gitarristin _gitarra_

das Saxopho[...]
zuxawfawn

der Saxophonist
zuxofonist

1: If you are talking about a female, add **in** (**innen** in the plural). **2**: Use the plural for
talking about types of beer. For ordering use the singular, e.g. **zwei Bier** (two beers).

bill (restaurant) **die Rechnung(en)** *rekhnoong*(en);
the bill please **zahlen bitte** *tsahlen bitta*
bin *der Eimer(-)* *eye-mer*
binoculars *das Fernglas(¨er)* *fairnglass*
PL: *fairnglayzer*
biodegradable *biologisch abbaubar*
bee-aw-lawgish upbaowbar
bird *der Vogel(¨)* *fawgel* PL: *furgel*
birthday *der Geburtstag(e)* *geboorts-*
tahg(a); happy birthday *herzlichen*
Glückwunsch zum Geburtstag *hairtslikhen*
glookvoonsh tsoom geboorts-tahg
biscuit *der Keks(e)* *kaiks*(a)
bit (as in "a bit of cake") *das Stück(e)* *shtook*(a),
OR (as in "a bit tired") *ein bißchen* *ine biss-khen*
to bite *beißen* *bye-ssen*; OR (insect) *stechen*
shtekhen
black *schwarz* *shvahrts*
blanket *die Decke(n)* *dekka*(n)
to bleed *bluten* *blooten*
blind *blind* *blint*
blister *die Blase(n)* *blahza*(n)
bloke *der Kerl(e)** *kairl*(a), OR *der Typ(en)**
toop(en)
blond *blond* *blont*
blood *das Blut* *bloot*; blood pressure *der*
Blutdruck *blootdrook*
blue *blau* *blaow*
to boast *an'geben* *ungaiben*
boat (big) *das Schiff(e)* *shiff*(a), OR (small)
das Boot(e) *bawt*(a) (See also sailing)

der Schlagzeuger
shlag-tsoyger

der Keyboarder
keeborder

das Keyboard
keebort

der Sänger
zenger

das Mikro*
meekraw

bike *das Fahrrad* — der Reifen *rye-fen*

die Lenkstange
lenk-shtunga
der Sattel
zuttel
das Rad
raht
die Kette
ketta
das Pedal
pedahl
die Trinkflasche
trink-flusha
die Luftpumpe
looft-poompa
die Bremse *bremza*
die Gangschaltung *gung-shultoong*

body *der Körper(-)* *kurper*
boiled *gekocht* *gekokht*
bone *der Knochen(-)* *knokh-en*, OR (fish) *die*
Gräte(n) *graita*(n)
book *das Buch(¨er)* *bookh* PL: *boohkher*
to book *buchen* *bookhen*
booked up *ausgebucht* *owssgebookht*
bookshop *die Buchhandlung(en)* *bookh-*
hundloong(en)
boot *der Stiefel(-)* *shteefel*
border (frontier) *die Grenze(n)* *grentsa*(n)
bored: to be bored *sich langweilen* *zikh*
lungvye-len
boring *langweilig* *lungvye-likh*
to borrow *sich leihen* *zikh lye-un*
boss (man) *der Chef(s)*[1] *shef*(s), OR *der Boß**
boss
both *beide* *by-da*; both of them *die beiden*
dee by-dun, OR *alle beide* *ullah by-da*
bottle *die Flasche(n)* *flusha*(n); bottle
opener *der Flaschenöffner(-)* *flushun-urfner*
bottom (not top) *der Boden* *bawden*, OR (bum)
*der Hintern(-)** *hintern*, OR *der Po(s)** *paw*(z)
bowl *die Schüssel(n)* *shoossel*(n)
bowling *Bowling* [n] *bowling*, OR *Kegeln* [n]
kaiguln
box office *die Kasse* *kussa*
boy *der Junge(n)* *yoonga*(n)
boyfriend *der Freund(e)* *froynd*(a)

3: If your sentence involves movement, use the accusative
case; if not, use the dative. For more about cases, see p. 44.

bra *der BH(-)* bay _hah_
brake *die Bremse(n)* _bremza_(n)
brave *tapfer* _tupfer_
bread (or loaf of bread) *das Brot(e)*
brawt(a); wholemeal bread *das*
Vollkornbrot(e) _folkorn-brawt_(a)
to break *brechen* _brekhen_, OR *kaputt'machen**
kupoot'mukhen; to break up (with someone)
Schluß machen* _shlooss_ mukhen
breakdown (car) *die Panne(n)* _punna_(n)
breakfast *das Frühstück(e)* _frooh_-shtook(a);
to have breakfast *frühstücken* _frooh_-shtooken
breast (bosom) *der Busen(-)* _boozen_, OR
(chest) *die Brust(¨e)* _broost_(a)
to breathe *atmen* _ahtmen_
bridge *die Brücke(n)* _brooka_(n)
bright (clever) *aufgeweckt* _aowf_gevekt, OR
(colour) *hell* _hel_
brilliant (fantastic) *genial* _gaineeyahl_, OR
toll* _toll_
to bring *bringen* _bring_-en
Britain *Großbritannien* [n] _grawssbritunnyen_
broke (no money) *pleite* _ply_-ta
broken *gebrochen* _gebrokhen_, OR *kaputt**
kupoott
brother *der Bruder(¨)* _brooder_ PL: _brooh_-der
brown *braun* _braown_
bruise *der blaue Fleck(en)* _blaowa_ _flek_(en)
brush *die Bürste(n)* _boohrsta_(n), OR
(paintbrush) *der Pinsel(-)* _pinzul_
bug (germ) *der Bazillus* _butsilooss_ PL: *Bazillen*
butsillen, OR (insect) *der Käfer(-)* _kaifer_
building *das Gebäude(-)* _geboyda_
bump (on head/body) *die Beule(n)* _boyla_(n),
OR (dent in car etc.) *die Delle(n)* _della_(n)
to bump into (something) *stoßen gegen*
[+ acc] _shtawssen_ gaigen, OR (someone by
chance) *zufällig treffen* _tsoofellikh_ treffen
to bunk off *schwänzen* _shventsen_
to burn *brennen* _brennen_
to burst *platzen* _plutsen_
bus *der Bus(se)* _booss_(a); by bus *mit dem Bus*
mit dem _booss_; bus station *der Busbahnhof(¨e)*
boossbahn-hawf PL: _boossbahn-hurfa_; bus stop *die*
Bushaltestelle(n) _booss_-hulta-shtella(n)
busy *beschäftigt* _besheftikht_
but *aber* _ahber_
butcher's *die Metzgerei(en)* _metsga-rye_(-un)
butter *die Butter* _bootter_
to buy *kaufen* _kaowfen_
by (as in "by the station") *bei* [+ dat] _by_, OR
(as in "saved by Indiana Jones") *von* [+dat] _fon_;
by my/your/himself/etc. *allein(e)* _ullyne_(-a)
bye *tschüs** _tshooss_, OR *tschau** _tshaow_

café *das Café(s)* _kufay_(s)
cake *der Kuchen(-)* _kookhen_, OR (gâteau) *die*
Torte(n) _tawrta_(n); cake shop *die*
Konditorei(en) _konditaw-rye_(-un); it's a piece
of cake *das ist ein Klacks** duss ist ine _kluks_
calculator *der Rechner(-)* _rekhner_
to call *rufen* _roofen_; to be called *heißen*
hye-sen
calm *ruhig* _roo-ikh_
calorie *die Kalorie(n)* _kuloree_(yan); low-
calorie *kalorienarm* _kuloreeyanarm_
camcorder *der Camcorder(-)* _kemkorder_
camera *die Kamera(s)* _kumairah_(s), OR *der*
Foto(s) _fawtaw_(s) (See also picture opposite)
to camp *zelten* _tselten_
campsite *der Campingplatz(¨e)* _kemping-_
pluts PL: _kemping-pletsa_, OR *der Zeltplatz(¨e)*
tseltpluts PL: _tseltpletsa_ (See also picture below)
can (of fruit, beer) *die Dose(n)* _dawza_(n); can
opener *der Dosenöffner(-)* _dawzen-urfner_
can (be able to) *können* _kurnun_ (See Modal
verbs p. 45)
canal *der Kanal(¨e)* _kunahl_ PL: _kunaila_
to cancel *ab'sagen* _upzahgen_
cancelled (bus, train etc.) *gestrichen*
geshtrikhen
candle *die Kerze(n)* _kairtsa_(n)
canoe *das Kanu(s)* _kahnoo_(s)
canoeing: to go canoeing *Kanu fahren*
kahnoo fahren, OR *paddeln* _puddeln_
cap (hat) *die Mütze(n)* _mootsa_(n)
capital (city) *die Hauptstadt(¨e)* _haowptshtut_
PL: _haowptshtetta_
car *das Auto(s)* _aowtaw_(s), OR *der Wagen(-)*
vahgen, OR (banger) *die Kiste(n)** _kissta_(n); car
park (open air) *der Parkplatz(¨e)* _parkpluts_
PL: _parkpletsa_, OR (multi-storey) *das*
Parkhaus(¨er) _parkhaowss_ PL: _parkhoyzer_

campsite *der Campingplatz*

die Sanitär-Anlagen
zuni_tair-unlahgun_

das Wohnmobil
vawn-maw_beel_

der Abfalleimer
upful-eye-mer

card *die Karte(n)* <u>kar</u>ta(n); credit card *die Kreditkarte(n)* kre<u>deet</u>-karta(n); card game *das Kartenspiel(e)* <u>kar</u>ten-shpeel(a)

care: I don't care! *das ist mir egal!* duss ist meer ay<u>gahl</u>, OR *das ist mir wurscht!** duss ist meer <u>voorsht</u>

careful *vorsichtig* <u>for</u>zikhtikh

carnival *der Karneval(e)* <u>kar</u>nevahl(a), OR *das Fest(e)* <u>fest</u>(a)

carrot *die Mohrrübe(n)* <u>maw</u>roohba(n), OR *die Karotte(n)* ku<u>rotta</u>(n)

to carry *tragen* <u>trah</u>gen

cartoon *der Cartoon(s)* kar<u>toon</u>(s), OR (film) *der Trickfilm(e)* <u>trick</u>film(e)

cash (money) *das Bargeld* <u>bar</u>-ghelt; to pay cash *bar bezahlen* <u>bar</u> be<u>tsah</u>len; cash desk *die Kasse(n)* <u>kussa</u>(n); cash dispenser *der Geldautomat(en)* ghelt-aowtaw<u>maht</u>(en)

cassette *die Kassette(n)* ku<u>ssetta</u>(n); cassette player *der Kassettenrecorder(-)* ku<u>ssetten</u>-raikorder

castle *das Schloß* <u>shloss</u> PL: *Schlösser* <u>shlursser</u>, OR (fortified) *die Burg(en)* <u>boorg</u>(en)

casual *lässig* <u>lessikh</u>, OR *cool** <u>kool</u>

cat *die Katze(n)* <u>kutsa</u>(n)

to catch *fangen* <u>fungen</u>

cathedral *der Dom(e)* <u>dawm</u>(a)

Catholic *katholisch* ku<u>taw</u>lish

cave *die Höhle(n)* <u>hurla</u>(n)

caving *Höhlenforschung* [f] <u>hurlen-forshoong</u>

CD *die CD(s)* tsee <u>dee</u>(s); CD-player *der CD Player(-)* tsee <u>dee</u> player

to celebrate *feiern* <u>fye</u>-ern

cellar *der Keller(-)* <u>keller</u>

cemetery *der Friedhof(¨e)* <u>freed</u>hawf PL: <u>freed</u>hurfa

centre *das Zentrum* <u>tsent</u>room PL: *Zentren* <u>tsent</u>ren

camera *die Kamera*

der Film <u>film</u>

das Zoom <u>tsoom</u> *der Blitz* <u>blits</u>

das Objektiv obyek<u>teef</u>

die Verschlußklappe fair<u>shloo</u>sskluppa *die Sonnenblende* <u>zonn</u>enblenda

century *das Jahrhundert(e)* yar<u>hoon</u>dert(a)

cereal (ask for it by name, e.g. Cornflakes)

certain *sicher* <u>sikher</u>

chair *der Stuhl(¨e)* <u>shtool</u> PL: <u>shtoo</u>hla

championship *die Meisterschaft(en)* <u>my</u>-ster-shufft(en)

chance (accident) *der Zufall(¨e)* <u>tsoo</u>ful PL: <u>tsoo</u>fella, OR (possibility) *die Chance(n)* <u>shonsa</u>(n), OR (risk) *das Risiko* <u>ree</u>zikaw PL: *Risiken* <u>ree</u>ziken; by chance *zufällig* <u>tsoo</u>fellikh

change *die Änderung(en)* <u>end</u>eroong(en), OR (money) *das Kleingeld* <u>klyne</u>-ghelt

to change (alter) *ändern* <u>end</u>ern, OR (money, wheel) *wechseln* <u>vex</u>eln, OR (train, bus) *um'steigen* <u>oom</u>shtye-gen, OR (to get changed) *sich um'ziehen* zikh <u>oom</u>tseeyen

changing-room (large) *der Umkleideraum(¨e)* <u>oom</u>klyda-raowm PL: <u>oom</u>klyda-royma, OR (small, individual) *die Umkleidekabine(n)* <u>oom</u>klyda-ku<u>beena</u>(n)

der Wasserkanister <u>vusser</u>-kunister — *der Holzhammer* <u>holts</u>-hummer — *die Anmeldung* <u>un</u>meldoong

der Gaskocher <u>gahz</u>-kokher — *das Zelt* <u>tselt</u> — *der Wohnwagen* <u>vawn</u>-vahgun

die Hängematte <u>zhenga</u>-mutta

CAMPING STERNBLICK

ANMELDUNG

der Hering <u>hai</u>ring

channel (TV) *das Programm(e)* progrum(a);
the Channel *der Ärmelkanal* airmel-kunahl
chaos *das Durcheinander* doorkh-ine-under,
OR *das Chaos* kah-oss
character *der Charakter(e)* kuruktair
PL: kuruktaira, OR (personality) *die
Persönlichkeit(en)* pairzurnlikh-kyte(n)
charity *der Wohltätigkeitsverein(e)*
vawltaytikh-kites-fair-ine(a)
charter (plane, flight) *Charter~* sharter~
charts (top records) *die Charts* [pl] charts
to chat *plaudern* plaowdern, OR *sich
unterhalten* zikh oonterhulten; to chat up
an'quatschen* unkvutshen
cheap *billig* billikh
to cheat *mogeln** mawguln
to check (a fact, date) *überprüfen* oohber-
proohfen, OR *checken** tsheken, OR (a passport,
ticket) *kontrollieren* kontrawleeren
check-in (at airport) *die Abfertigung(en)*
upfair-tigoong(en)
check-out (cash register) *die Kasse(n)* kussa(n)
cheeky *frech* frekh
cheers *prost* prawst
cheer up! *Kopf hoch!* kopf hawkh
cheese *der Käse* kaiza
cheesecake *der Käsekuchen* kaiza-kookhen
chemist's *die Drogerie(n)* droggeree(yun), OR
(for prescriptions) *die Apotheke(n)* upawtaika(n)
cheque *der Scheck(s)* shek(s); cheque-book
das Scheckbuch("er) shek-bookh PL: shek-booh-kher
cherry *die Kirsche(n)* keersha(n)
chess *Schach* [n] shahkh
chest (part of body) *die Brust("e)* broost(a)
chewing gum *das Kaugummi* kaowgoomee
chicken (roast, grilled) *das Hähnchen(-)*
hainkhen, OR (live, boiled) *das Huhn("er)* hoon
PL: hooh-ner
child *das Kind(er)* kint PL: kinder
chips (French fries) *Pommes frites* pom frit, OR
Pommes* pomuss, OR (potato crisps) *Chips* tships
chocolate *die Schokolade(n)* shokawlahda,
OR (as in "a box of chocolates") *die Praline(n)*
prahleena(n)
choice *die Wahl* vahl
choir *der Chor("e)* kor PL: kur-a
to choose *wählen* vailen
chop (pork/lamb) *das Kotelett(s)* kotlet(s)
Christian *christlich* kristlikh ·
Christmas *Weihnachten* [n] vye-nukhten
to chuck (throw) *schmeißen* shmye-sen, OR
(finish with a girl/boyfriend) *Schluß machen
mit* shlooss mukhen mit, E.G. she's chucked him
sie hat mit ihm Schluß gemacht ·

church *die Kirche* keerkha(n)
cider (apple wine) *der Apfelwein* upfelvine
cigarette *die Zigarette(n)* tsiggaretta(n), OR
die Kippe(n)* kippa(n)
cinema *das Kino(s)* keenaw(s)
circus *der Zirkus(se)* tseerkooss(a)
city *die Großstadt("e)* grawshtut PL: grawshtetta
classical *klassisch* klussish
clean *sauber* zaowber
clever *klug* kloog, OR (crafty) *schlau* shlaow
cliff *der Felsen(-)* felzun
climber (rock) *der Kletterer(-)[1]* kletterer, OR
(mountain) *der Bergsteiger(-)[1]* bairgshtye-ger
climbing (rock) *Klettern* [n] klettern, OR
(mountain) *Bergsteigen* [n] bairg-shtygen (See
also picture opposite)
cloakroom *die Garderobe(n)* gardarawba(n)
close (physically) *in der Nähe* in dair naya, OR
(mentally) *eng* eng; close friends
engbefreundet engbafroyndet
to close *zu'machen* tsoomukhen
closed *geschlossen* geshlossen, OR *zu* tsoo
clothes *Kleider* klyder, OR *Klamotten**
klumotten
cloud *die Wolke(n)* volka(n)
club *der Verein(e)* fair-ine(-a), OR *der
Club(s)** kloob(s)
clubbing: to go clubbing *in Clubs gehen*
in kloobs gayen
coach (bus) *der Reisebus(se)* ryzabooss(a) OR
der Bus(se) booss(a), OR (trainer) *der Trainer(-)[1]*
trainer
coast *die Küste(n)* koosta(n)
coat *der Mantel(")* muntel PL: mentel
code *der Code(s)* kawd(s), OR (post/area code)
die Postleitzahl(en) posst-lite-tsahl(en), OR (for
phoning) *die Vorwahl(en)* forvahl(en)
co-ed (mixed) *gemischt* gemisht
coffee *der Kaffee* kuffay, OR (coffee
flavoured) *Mokka~* mokkah
coin *die Münze(n)* moontsa(n)
coincidence *der Zufall("e)* tsooful PL: tsoofella
cold *kalt* kult; to have cold feet (about
something) *kalte Füße kriegen* kulta foohssa
kreegen
cold (illness) *die Erkältung(en)* airkeltoong(en);
to have a cold *erkältet sein* airkeltet zyne
to collect (stamps etc.) *sammeln* zummeln
colour *die Farbe(n)* farba(n)
colourful *bunt* boont
comb *der Kamm("e)* kum PL: kemma
to come *kommen* kommen; to come back
zurück'kommen tsoorook-kommen; to come in
(he)rein'kommen[2] (hair)rine-kommen

1: If you are talking about a female, add *in* (*innen* in the plural). **2**: In spoken German you
often drop the *he* and say *reinkommen*.

comfortable *bequem* bai-*kvaim*; to feel comfortable *sich wohl fühlen* zikh *vawl* foolen

comic book *der Comic(s)* *komik*(s)

common (not unusual) *häufig* *hoy*fikh

compass *der Kompaß* PL: *Kompasse* *kom*-pus(-a)

competition *der Wettbewerb* *vet*bevairb, OR (people you are up against) *die Konkurrenz* konkoo*rents*

to complain *sich beklagen* zikh be*klahgen*

completely *völlig* *furlikh*

compulsory *obligatorisch* obligu*tawrish*, OR *Pflicht~* *pflikht*

computer *der Computer(-)* kom*pyooter*; computer studies *die Informatik* informah*teek*

concert *das Konzert(e)* kont*sairt*(a)

condom *das Präservativ(e)* prayzairva*teef* PL: prayzairva*teeva*, OR *das Kondom(e)* kon*dawm*(a), OR *der Gummi(s)** *goo*mee(s)

to confuse *verwirren* fair*virrun*

to congratulate *gratulieren* grutoo*leeren*

congratulations *herzliche Glückwünsche* *hairts*likha *glook*voonsha

connection (train, plane) *der Anschluß* PL: *Anschlüsse* *un*shlooss(a)

conservation *der Umweltschutz* *oom*velt-shootts

constipated *verstopft* fair*shtopft*

consulate *das Konsulat(e)* konzoo*laht*(a)

contact lens *die Kontaktlinse(n)* kon*tukt*linza(n); soft/hard *weich/hart* *vye-kh*/*hart*; cleansing solution *Reinigungslösung* *rye*-nigoongz-*lerzoong*; rinsing solution *Abspüllösung* *up*shpoohl-*lerzoong*

contagious *ansteckend* *un*shtekend

contemporary (same age) *gleichaltrig* *glykh*-ultrikh, OR (people, things) *zeitgenössisch* *tsyte*-ge*nurss*ish

to continue *weiter'machen* *vyter*-mukhen

contraception *die Empfängnisverhütung* emp*feng*nis-fair*hoohtoong*

conversation *das Gespräch(e)* ge*shpraikh*(a)

to cook *kochen* *kokhen*

cookie *der Keks(e)* *kaiks*(a)

cool (trendy, relaxed) *cool** *kool*

to cope *zurecht'kommen* tsoo*rekht*-kommen

to copy *kopieren* ko*peeren*

cork (in bottle) *der Korken(-)* *korken*

corkscrew *der Korkenzieher(-)* *korken*-tseeyer

corner *die Ecke(n)* *ekke*(n)

correct *richtig* *rikh*tikh

cosmopolitan *kosmopolitisch* kozmawpaw*lee*tish

to cost *kosten* *kosten*

climbing *das Klettern*

der Kletterer *kletterer*

der Helm *helm*

die Schlinge *shling-a*

die Kreide *kry-da*

die Kreidetasche *kry-da-tusha*

der Sitzgurt *zitsgoort*

der Felsen *felzen*

der Karabiner *kuru*beener

der Kletterschuh *kletter*-shoo

das Kletterseil *kletter*-zyle

cotton (material) *die Baumwolle*
_baowm_volla; cotton wool *die Watte* _vutta_
to count *zählen* _tsailen_
country *das Land(¨er)* _lunt_ PL: _lender_
course (series of lessons) *der Kurs(e)* _koorss_
PL: _koorza_, OR (meal) *der Gang(¨e)* _gung_
PL: _genga_; of course *natürlich* _nutoohr_lihk
court (sports) *der Platz(¨e)* _pluts_ PL: _pletsa_
cousin (man) *der Cousin(s)* _koozang_(s), OR
(woman) *die Cousine(n)* _koozeena_(n)
to cover *bedecken* _bedecken_
cow *die Kuh(¨e)* _koo_ PL: _kooh-a_
coward *der Feigling(e)* _fye_-gling(a)
to crack (lose control, give in) *durch'drehen**
doorkh-drayen; to crack a joke *einen Witz*
reißen _ine-un vits_ ryssen; to crack up (laugh)
sich tot'lachen zikh _tawt_-lukhen
cramp *der Krampf(¨e)* _krumpf_ PL: _krempf_(a)
crazy *verrückt* fair_ookt_, OR *irre* _irra_; to be
crazy about (a person) *ganz wild auf* [+ acc]
sein gunts _vilt_ aowf ... zyne; you must be crazy!
du bist wohl verrückt! doo bist vawl fair_ookt_
cream (on milk) *die Sahne* _zahna_, OR (lotion)
die Creme _kraim_
credit card (See card)
creepy *unheimlich* _oon_-hyme-likh
crime *das Verbrechen(-)* fair_brekhen_
crisis *die Krise(n)* _kreeza_(n)
crisps *Chips* _tships_
to criticize *kritisieren* krit_eezeeren_
cross (angry) *böse* _burza_, OR (annoyed)
sauer* _zaower_, OR (sign) *das Kreuz(e)* _kroyts_(a)
to cross *überqueren* oohber-_kvairen_
crossing (by sêa) *die Überfahrt(en)*
oohber_fahrt_(en) (See also pedestrian)
crossroads *die Kreuzung(en)* _kroytsoong_(en)
crossword *das Kreuzworträtsel(-)*
_kroyts_vort-raitsel
cruel *grausam* _graow_zahm
crush: I've got a crush on him/her *ich
schwärme für ihn/sie* ikh-_shvairma_ foohr een/zee
to cry (weep) *weinen* _vye_-nen
cucumber *die Gurke(n)* _goorka_(n)
cult *der Kult(e)* _koollt_(a)
cultural *kulturell* koollt_oorell_
culture *die Kultur(en)* koollt_oor_(en)
cup *die Tasse(n)* _tussa_(n)
cupboard *der Schrank(¨e)* _shrunk_ PL: _shrenka_
curious (inquisitive) *neugierig* _noygeerikh_
custom *der Brauch(¨e)* _braowkh_ PL: _broykha_
customs *der Zoll* _tsol_
to cut *schneiden* _shnyden_
Czech: the Czech Republic *die
Tschechische Republik* _tshekhisha repoobleek_

damn! *verdammt noch mal!** fair_dumt_
nokh mahl
to dance *tanzen* _tuntsen_
dancer *der Tänzer(-)*[1] _tentser_
dangerous *gefährlich* gef_airlikh_
to dare (risk) *riskieren* riss_keeren_, OR (be bold
enough) *wagen* _vahgen_; I dare you! *Feigling!*
fye-gling
dark *dunkel* _doonkel_
darts: to play darts *pfeil'werfen* _pfyle_-vairfen
date *das Datum* _dahtoom_ PL: *Daten* _dahten_,
OR (meeting with boy/girlfriend) *die
Verabredung(en)* fair-_upraidoong_(en), OR *das
Date(s)**; date of birth *das Geburtsdatum*
geboorts-_dahtoom_; what's the date today? *den
wievielten haben wir heute?* dain vee_feelten_
hahben veer _hoyta_; up to date (current)
aktuell uktoo-_ell_; out of date (no longer valid)
nicht mehr gültig nikht mair _gooltikh_
day *der Tag(e)* _tahg_(a)
dead *tot* _tawt_
deaf *taub* _taowp_
dear *lieb* _leeb_
decaffeinated *koffeinfrei* koff_ayeenfry_
December *Dezember* [m] det_sember_
to decide *beschließen* be_shleessen_
deck (on boat) *das Deck(s)* _dek_(s); deck chair
der Liegestuhl(¨e) _leega_-shtool PL: _leega_-shtoohla
deep *tief* _teef_
degree *der Grad(e)* _graht_ PL: _grahda_
delay *die Verspätung(en)* fair-_shpaitoong_(en)
delicatessen *das Delikatessengeschäft(e)*
dayleekah_tessen_-ge_sheft_(a)
delicious *köstlich* _kurst_likh, OR *lecker* _lekker_
democracy *die Demokratie* daymawkrah_tee_
demonstration *die Demonstration(en)*
dai-mon-strat_seeyawn_(en), OR *die Demo(s)**
daimaw(s)
denim *der Jeansstoff(e)* _jeans_htoff(a)
Denmark *Dänemark* [n] _daina_mark
dentist (man) *der Zahnarzt(¨e)* _tsahn_artst
PL: _tsahn_airt-sta, OR (woman) *die Zahnärztin(nen)*
_tsahn_airtstin(nen)
deodorant *das Deodorant(s)* day-
awdaw_runt_(s), OR *das Deo(s)**
department store *das Kaufhaus(¨er)*
kaowf-haowss PL: _kaowf_-hoyzer
departure *die Abfahrt(en)* _upfahrt_(en), OR
(plane) *der Abflug(¨e)* _upfloog_ PL: _upflooh_-ga;
departure lounge (at airport) *die
Abflughalle(n)* _upfloog_-hulla(n)
to depend it depends *es kommt darauf an*
ess _komt dahraowf un_
deposit (money as guarantee) *die*

1: If you are talking about a female, add *in* (*innen* in the plural).

Kaution(en) kaowtsee-_awn_(en), OR (money given in advance) **die Anzahlung(en)** _un_tsah-loong(en)
depressing deprimierend deprim_ee_rend
to describe beschreiben be-_shrye_-ben
desk der Schreibtisch(e) _shrype_-tish(a)
dessert der Nachtisch(e) _nahkh_-tish(a)
detail das Detail(s) dai-_tye_(s)
detour (for traffic) **die Umleitung(en)** _oom_lye-toong(en), OR (on foot) **der Umweg(e)** _oom_vaig(a)
diabetic zuckerkrank _tsooker_-krunk
dialect der Dialekt(e) deeyahl_ekt_(a)
dialling tone das Amtszeichen(-) _umt_stsye-khen
diarrhoea (US: diarrhea) **Durchfall** [m] _doorkh_ful
diary der Terminkalender(-) tairmeen-_kulender_, OR der Kalender(-), OR (private book) **das Tagebuch(¨er)** _tahga_bookh PL: _tahga_booh-kher
dice der Würfel(-) _voohr_fel
dictionary das Wörterbuch(¨er) _vurter_-bookh PL: _vurter_-booh-kher
diesel (fuel) **der Diesel** _deezel_
diet die Diät(en) dee-_ait_(en)
different verschieden fair_sheeden_; different from/to anders als _unders_ ults
difficult schwierig _shvee_rikh
dining room das Eßzimmer(-) _ess_-tsimmer
dinner (evening meal) **das Abendessen(-)** _ah_bend-essen, OR das Essen(-) _essen_, OR (midday meal) **das Mittagessen(-)** _mittahg_-essen
direction die Richtung(en) _rikh_toong(en)
director (of film) **der Regisseur(e)**¹ rayzhis_ur_(a)
dirty schmutzig _shmoot_sikh

disabled behindert be_hindert_
disadvantage der Nachteil(e) _nukh_-tyle(-a)
disappointed enttäuscht ent_toysht_
disaster die Katastrophe(n) kutu_strawfa_(n), OR (accident, tragedy) **das Unglück(e)** _oon_glook(a)
disc jockey der Discjockey(s)
disco die Disco(s) _disskaw_(s)
discount der Rabatt(e) ru_butt_(a)
to discover entdecken ent_dekken_
discrimination die Diskriminierung diskrimin_ee_roong
to discuss diskutieren disk_oo_teeren
disgusting ekelhaft _aikel_huft; disgusting! **Schweinerei!*** shvyna-_rye_
dish (plate) **die Schüssel(n)** _shoos_sell(n), OR (meal) **das Gericht(e)** ge_rikht_(a)
disk: floppy disk **die Diskette(n)** disk_etta_(n)
distance die Entfernung(en) ent_fair_noong(en)
to disturb stören _shturen_
to dive (into water) **springen** _shpringen_, OR (scuba dive) **tauchen** _taowkhen_
diving (scuba diving) **Tauchen** [n] _taowkhen_ (See also picture below)
divorced geschieden ge_sheeden_

---

diving Tauchen [n]

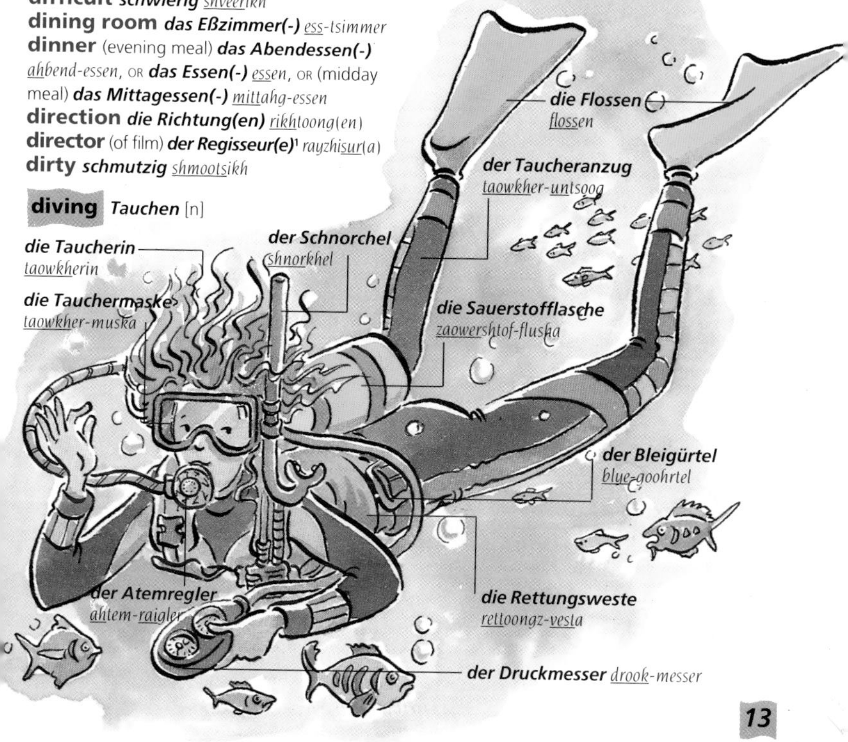

die Flossen (-)
flossen

der Taucheranzug
taowkher-untsoog

die Taucherin
taowkherin

der Schnorchel
shnorkhel

die Taucgermaske
taowkher-muska

die Sauerstofflasche
_zaower_shtof-flusha

der Bleigürtel
blue-goohrtel

der Atemregler
ahtem-raigler

die Rettungsweste
rettoongz-vesta

der Druckmesser
drook-messer

dizzy *schwindlig* <u>shv</u>indlikh
to do *machen* <u>mukh</u>en, OR *tun* <u>toon</u> (See also Verbs p.45); to do up *zu'machen* <u>tsoo</u>-mukhen
doctor (man) *der Arzt("e)* <u>artst</u> PL: <u>airtst</u>a, OR (woman) *die Ärztin(nen)* <u>airtst</u>in(en)
dodgy (dubious) *zweifelhaft* <u>tsvy</u>felhuft, OR (risky) *riskant* risk<u>unt</u>
dog *der Hund(e)* <u>hoont</u> PL: <u>hoond</u>a
dole: to be on the dole *stempeln gehen* <u>shtemp</u>eln gayen
door *die Tür(en)* <u>toohr</u>(en)
double *Doppel~* <u>dopp</u>el E.G. double bed *das Doppelbett*
down: to go/walk down *hinunter'gehen* hin<u>oont</u>er-gayen; to be/feel down *sich niedergeschlagen fühlen* zikh <u>need</u>er-geshlahgen foohlen, OR *down sein* <u>down</u> zyne
draw (score) *unentschieden* <u>oon</u>ent-shee-den
to draw (a picture) *zeichnen* <u>tsye</u>-kh-nen
dream *der Traum("e)* <u>traowm</u> PL: <u>troy</u>ma
dress *das Kleid(er)* <u>klyde</u>(-er)
to dress (get dressed) *sich an'ziehen* zikh <u>un</u>-tseeyen
drink *das Getränk(e)* ge<u>trenk</u>(a)
to drink *trinken* <u>trink</u>en
to drive *fahren* <u>fahr</u>en, OR (to go by car) *mit dem Auto fahren* mit dem <u>aow</u>taw fahren
driver *der Fahrer(-)*[1] <u>fahr</u>er
to drop (let fall) *fallen lassen* <u>ful</u>en <u>luss</u>en, OR (let go of) *los'lassen* <u>lawss</u>-lussen; to drop in (visit) *vorbei'kommen* for<u>bye</u>-kommen; to drop (someone) off *ab'setzen* <u>up</u>-zetsen
drug *die Droge(n)* <u>drawg</u>a(n); drug addict *der/die Drogensüchtige(n)* drawgun-<u>zookht</u>iga(n)
drunk *betrunken* be<u>troonk</u>en, OR *besoffen* be<u>zoff</u>en; to get drunk *sich betrinken* zikh be<u>trink</u>en, OR *blau werden* <u>blaow</u>-vairden, OR *sich besaufen* zikh be<u>zaow</u>fen
dry *trocken* <u>trock</u>en
dubbed *synchronisiert* zoonkroneezeert
dump (for rubbish/garbage) *der Müllplatz("e)* <u>murl</u>pluts PL: <u>murl</u>pletsa, OR (dull/awful town) *das Kaff(s)* <u>kuf</u>(s), OR (dull/awful room) *das Dreckloch("er)* <u>drek</u>lokh PL: <u>drek</u>lurkher
dungarees *die Latzhose(n)* <u>luts</u>-hawza(n)
Dutch *holländisch* <u>holl</u>endish, OR (man) *Holländer(-)* <u>holl</u>ender, OR (woman) *Holländerin(nen)* <u>holl</u>enderin(nen)
duty-free *zollfrei* <u>tsolf</u>ry
dying: to be dying to (do something) *darauf brennen (etwas) zu (tun)* dah<u>raowf</u> brennen (<u>etvuss</u>) tsoo (<u>toon</u>); to be dying of hunger/thirst *vor Hunger/Durst sterben* for <u>hoong</u>er/<u>doorst</u>-shtairben

each (as in "each day/man") *jeder* [m] <u>yai</u>der, OR *jede* [f] <u>yai</u>da, OR *jedes* [n] <u>yai</u>dus, OR (as in "they have two each") *je* <u>yay</u>, OR (as in "they cost one mark each") *das Stück* duss <u>shtook</u>
ear *das Ohr(en)* <u>awr</u>(un) (See also to ache)
early *früh* <u>frooh</u>, OR (ahead of time) *zu früh* <u>tsoo frooh</u>
to earn *verdienen* fair-<u>deen</u>en
earphones *der Kopfhörer(-)* <u>kopf</u>-hur-er
east *der Osten* <u>ost</u>en
Easter *Ostern* [n] <u>awst</u>ern
easy *leicht* <u>lye</u>-kht
easy-going *ungezwungen* <u>oon</u>-getsvoongen
to eat *essen* <u>ess</u>en (See also Verbs p. 45), OR (guzzle) *fressen* <u>fress</u>en
ecology *die Ökologie* urkolaw<u>ghee</u>

egg *das Ei*

das hartgekochte Ei <u>hartg</u>ekokhta <u>eye</u>

das Spiegelei <u>shpeegul</u>-<u>eye</u>

das Rührei <u>roor</u>-eye

das verlorene Ei fair<u>lorena</u> <u>eye</u>

education (upbringing) *die Erziehung* airts<u>eeyoong</u>, OR (studies) *die Ausbildung* <u>aowss</u>bildoong; higher education (academic) *die höhere Bildung* <u>hooera</u> <u>bildoong</u>; further education *die Fortbildung* <u>fort</u>bildoong
egg *das Ei(er)* <u>eye</u>(-er) (See also picture above)
elbow *der Ellenbogen(-)* <u>ellen</u>bawgen
election *die Wahl(en)* <u>vahl</u>(en)
electric *elektrisch* ay<u>lek</u>trish
electricity *der Strom* <u>shtrawm</u>
elevator *der Lift(s)* <u>lift</u>(s)
else *sonst* <u>zonst</u> E.G. anything else? *sonst noch etwas?*
embarrassed *verlegen* fair<u>laigen</u>
embarrassing *peinlich* <u>pyne</u>-likh
embassy *die Botschaft(en)* <u>bawt</u>shufft(en)

1: If you are talking about a female, add *in* (*innen* in the plural).

emergency *der Notfall(¨e)* <u>nawt</u>-ful PL: <u>nawt</u>-fella; emergency exit *der Notausgang(¨e)* <u>nawt</u>-<u>aowssgaung</u> PL: <u>nawt</u>-<u>aowssgaeng</u>-a

empty *leer* <u>lair</u>

end (of story) *der Schluß* <u>shlooss</u>, OR (of road, month) *das Ende* <u>enda</u>, OR (of finger, pen) *die Spitze(n)* <u>shpitsa</u>(n)

engine (of car) *der Motor(en)* <u>mawtor</u>(en)

England *England* [n] <u>englunt</u>

English *englisch* <u>english</u>, OR (man) *Engländer(-)* <u>englender</u>, OR (woman) *Engländerin(nen)* <u>englenderin</u>(nen); in English *auf englisch*

to enjoy (yourself) *sich amüsieren* zikh umoo<u>zeeren</u>

enough *genug* ga-<u>noog</u>; that's enough *das reicht* duss <u>rye</u>-kht

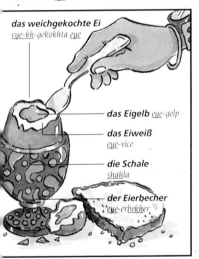

das weichgekochte Ei
<u>vye</u>-<u>kh</u>-gekokhta <u>eye</u>

das Eigelb <u>eye</u>-gelp

das Eiweiß
<u>eye</u>-vice

die Schale
<u>shahla</u>

der Eierbecher
<u>eye</u>-erbekher

entertainment *die Unterhaltung* oonter-<u>hulltoong</u>

envelope *der Umschlag(¨e)* <u>oom</u>shlahg PL: <u>oom</u>shlaiga

environment *die Umwelt* <u>oom</u>velt

epileptic *epileptisch* aypee<u>lep</u>tish; epileptic fit *der epileptische Anfall* aypee<u>lep</u>tisha <u>un</u>ful

equal *gleich* <u>glye</u>-kh

erotic *erotisch* air<u>aw</u>tish

escalator *die Rolltreppe(n)* <u>roll</u>treppa(n)

essential *unbedingt erforderlich* <u>oon</u>bedinkt airf<u>order</u>likh

EU *die EU* <u>ay</u> <u>ooh</u>

Europe *Europa* [n] oy<u>raw</u>pah; eastern Europe *Osteuropa* ost-oy<u>raw</u>pah

European *europäisch* oyraw<u>pay</u>ish, OR

(man) *Europäer(-)* [m] oy<u>raw</u>payer, OR (woman) *Europäerin(nen)* [f] oyraw<u>pay</u>erin(nen)

evening *der Abend(e)* <u>ah</u>bent PL: <u>ah</u>benda

everybody *alle* <u>ulla</u>, OR (stressed, as in "everybody knows") *jeder* <u>yaider</u>

everything *alles* <u>ull</u>uss

everywhere *überall* oohber-<u>ul</u>

to exaggerate *übertreiben* oohber-<u>try</u>-ben

exam *die Prüfung(en)* <u>proohfoong</u>(en)

example *das Beispiel(e)* <u>by</u>-shpeel(a); for example *zum Beispiel*

excellent *ausgezeichnet* aowss-getsye-kh-net, OR *exzellent* ex-ts<u>ai</u>lent

except *außer* [+ dat] <u>aowsser</u>

excess: excess weight *das Übergewicht* oohber-ge<u>vikht</u>; excess fare *die Nachlösegebühr(en)* nakhlurza-ge<u>boohr</u>(en)

exchange (holiday) *der Austausch* <u>aowss</u>taowsh; foreign exchange office *die Wechselstube(n)* <u>vexel</u>-shtooba(n); exchange rate *der Wechselkurs(e)* <u>vexel</u>-koorz(a)

excited *aufgeregt* <u>aowf</u>gayraykt; to get excited *sich auf regen* zikh <u>aowf</u>-raygun

exciting *aufregend* <u>aowf</u>raygent

excuse *die Entschuldigung(en)* ent<u>shool</u>digoong(en); excuse me! *Entschuldigung!*

exercise *die Übung(en)* <u>ooh</u>boong(en)

exhausted *erschöpft* air<u>shurpft</u>, OR *(total) kaputt** (tawt<u>ahl</u>) ku<u>poot</u>

exhibition *die Ausstellung(en)* <u>aowss</u>shtelloong(en)

exit *der Ausgang(¨e)* <u>aowss</u>gaung PL: <u>aowss</u>gaeng-a

exotic *exotisch* ex<u>aw</u>tish

expensive *teuer* <u>toy</u>er

experience *die Erfahrung(en)* air<u>fah</u>roong(en)

to explain *erklären* air<u>klairen</u>

to explore *erforschen* air<u>forshen</u>

extra (additional) *zusätzlich* <u>tsoo</u>zetslikh, OR (spare or especially) *extra* <u>ek</u>strah

eye *das Auge(n)* <u>aow</u>-ga(n)

fabulous *fabelhaft* <u>fah</u>bel-huft

face *das Gesicht(er)* ge<u>zikht</u>(er)

to fail (exam) *durch fallen* <u>doorkh</u>-fulun

to faint *ohnmächtig werden* <u>awn</u>mekhtikh <u>vairden</u>; I feel faint *mir ist schwach* meer ist <u>shvukh</u>

fair (just) *gerecht* gay<u>rekht</u>, OR *fair* <u>fair</u>

faithful *treu* <u>troy</u>

to fall *fallen* <u>fulun</u>; to fall for (a person) *sich in* [+ acc] *verlieben* zikh in ... fair<u>leeben</u>, OR *sich in* [+ acc] *verknallen** zikh in ... fair<u>knullen</u>, OR (a trick) *herein fallen auf* [+ acc] hair-<u>ine</u>-fulun aowf; to fall out with (a person) *sich zerstreiten* zikh tsair-<u>shtryte</u>-en

family *die Familie(n)* fu<u>mee</u>leeya(n)
famous (a star) *berühmt* be<u>roo</u>hmt, OR (well-known) *bekannt* be<u>kunt</u>
fan (supporter, enthusiast) *der Fan(s)* <u>fan</u>(s)
to fancy (in German you say that "someone appeals to you") *gefallen* [+ dat] ge<u>fu</u>lun, E.G. he fancies Anna *Anna gefällt ihm*; do you fancy (doing something)? *hast du Lust ...?* hust doo <u>loost</u> ...
fantastic *phantastisch* fun<u>tus</u>tish
far *weit* <u>vyte</u>
fare *der Fahrpreis(e)* <u>far</u>-price PL: <u>far</u>prye-za ; full/half fare *zum vollen/halben Preis* tsoom <u>foll</u>en/<u>hulb</u>en price
fashion *die Mode(n)* <u>maw</u>da(n)
fashionable *modisch* <u>maw</u>dish
fast *schnell* <u>shnell</u>
fat (on meat) *das Fett* <u>fet</u>, OR (large) *dick* <u>dik</u>
father *der Vater(¨)* <u>fah</u>ter PL: <u>fai</u>ter
favourite *Lieblings~* <u>leeb</u>lings, E.G. my favourite hat *mein Lieblingshut*
February *Februar* [m] <u>fai</u>broo-ar
fed: to be fed up *die Nase voll haben** dee <u>nah</u>za <u>fol</u> hahben
to feel (as in "to feel happy/good") *sich fühlen* zikh <u>fooh</u>-len (See also to touch)
feminist (woman) *die Feministin(nen)* femin-<u>isstin</u>(en), OR (man) *der Feminist(en)* femin-<u>isst</u>(en)
ferry *die Fähre(n)* <u>faira</u>(n)
fever *das Fieber(-)* <u>fee</u>ber
few (not many) *wenige* <u>vain</u>iga; a few (as in "I'd like a few") *ein paar* ine <u>par</u>, OR (as in "a few cakes/people") *einige* <u>ine</u>-iga
fight (punch-up) *die Schlägerei(en)* shlaiger-<u>eyel</u>(-en)

first aid kit *das Erste-Hilfe-Set*

die Wundsalbe <u>voond</u>-zulba
die Pinzette pin-<u>tsetta</u>
das Pflaster <u>pflu</u>ster
die Schmerztablette shm<u>airts</u>-tubletta
der Verband <u>fair</u>bunt
die Schere <u>shaira</u>
das Thermometer <u>tairmo</u>maiter

football (soccer) *Fußball*

der Spieler <u>shpee</u>ler
das Tor <u>tor</u>
der Tormann <u>tor</u>mun
der Fußball <u>foos</u>sbul

to fight *kämpfen* <u>kemp</u>fen
to fill (bottle) *füllen* <u>fooll</u>en; to fill up (with fuel) *volltanken* <u>foll</u>tunken
film *der Film(e)* <u>film</u>(a)
to find *finden* <u>fin</u>den; to find out (get information) *sich erkundigen* zikh air<u>koon</u>digen, OR (discover) *heraus'finden* hair<u>aowss</u>-finden
fine (penalty) *die Geldstrafe(n)* <u>gelt</u>-shtrahfa(n), OR (OK) *gut* <u>goot</u> (See also weather picture)
finger *der Finger(-)* <u>fing</u>-er
to finish *fertig'machen* <u>fair</u>tikh-mukhen
fire *das Feuer(-)* <u>foy</u>er; fire brigade *die Feuerwehr* <u>foy</u>-ervair; fire exit *der Notausgang(¨e)* <u>nawt</u>-aowss-gung PL: <u>nawt</u>-aowss-genga
fireworks (display) *das Feuerwerk* <u>foy</u>er-vairk
first (as in "the first man/book") *erste(n)* <u>airst</u>a(n), OR (firstly) *zuerst* tsoo-<u>airst</u>
first aid *Erste Hilfe* [f] <u>airsta-hilfa</u>; first aid kit *das Erste-Hilfe-Set* <u>airsta hilfa</u> set (See also picture left)
fish *der Fisch(e)* <u>fish</u>(a)
to fish *fischen* <u>fish</u>en, OR *angeln* <u>ung</u>-eln
fit (tantrum) *der Wutanfall(¨e)* <u>voot</u>-un-fal PL: <u>voot</u>-un-fella, OR (on form physically) *fit* <u>fit</u>; to be in fits (of laughter) *sich kaputt'lachen** zikh ku<u>poot</u>-lukhen
to fit *passen* <u>pus</u>-en
to fix (mend) *in Ordnung bringen* in <u>ord</u>noong bringen, OR (arrange a time/date) *aus'machen* <u>aowss</u>-mukhen
fizzy *mit Kohlensäure* mit <u>kawl</u>en-<u>zoyra</u>; fizzy drink *der Sprudel* <u>shproo</u>del
flat (apartment) *die Wohnung(en)* <u>vaw</u>noong(en), OR (not round) *flach* <u>flukh</u>, OR (tyre) *platt* <u>plut</u>

1: If you are talking about a female, add *in* (*innen* in the plural).

der Fan _fan_

football (American)
American Football

das Schulterpolster _shoolter-polster_

Cheerleader _cheerleader_

der Helm _helm_

die Maske _muska_

der Stollen _shtollen_

der Schiedsrichter _sheeds-rikhter_

das Trikot _treekaw_

flavour der Geschmack("e) _geshmuk_ PL: _geshmekka_, OR (ice cream) **die Sorte(n)** _zorta(n)_

flea market der Flohmarkt("e) _flaw-markt_ PL: _flaw-mairkta_

flight der Flug("e) _floog_ PL: _floohga_

to flirt flirten _flurten_

floor (level) der Stock(-) _shtok_

flop (failure) der Reinfall("e) _rine-ful_ PL: _rine-fella_, OR der Flop(s)* _flop_(s)

flower die Blume(n) _blooma_(n)

flu die Grippe _grippa_

fluently fließend _fleessent_

fly die Fliege(n) _fleega_(n)

to fly fliegen _fleegen_

to follow folgen [+ dat] _folgen_

food das Essen _essen_; food-poisoning **die Lebensmittelvergiftung** _laibenz-mittel-fair-giftoong_

foot der Fuß("e) _fooss_ PL: _fooh-sa_; on foot **zu Fuß** _tsoo fooss_; to put your foot in it **einen Bock schießen*** _ine-nen bok-sheessen_

football (soccer) **Fußball** [m] _foossbul_; American football **American Football** [m] (See also picture above)

for für _foohr_, OR (as in "I have been waiting for two hours") **seit** [+ dat] _zyte_; what for? **wozu?** _vaw-tsoo_

forbidden verboten _fairbawten_

foreigner der Ausländer(-)¹ _aowss-lender_

forest der Wald("er) _vult_ PL: _velder_

to forget vergessen _fair-gessen_

to forgive verzeihen _fair-tsye-en_

fork die Gabel(n) _gahbel_(n)

fountain der Brunnen(-) _broonen_

frame (picture, bike) der Rahmen(-) _rahm-en_, OR (glasses) das Gestell(e) _geshtell_(a)

France Frankreich [n] _frunk-rye-kh_

to freak out (lose your cool) **durch'drehen*** _doorkh-drayen_, OR **aus'flippen*** _aowss-flippen_

free frei _fru_

to freeze frieren _freeren_

French französisch _fruntsurzish_; French fries **Pommes frites** _pomfrit_, OR **Pommes*** _pom_uss

fresh frisch _frish_

Friday Freitag [m] _fry-tahg_

fridge der Kühlschrank("e) _koohl-shrunk_ PL: _koohl-shrenka_

fried Brat~ _braht_, E.G. fried potatoes **Bratkartoffeln** (See also egg picture)

friend der Freund(e)¹ _froynd_(a), OR (acquaintance) **der/die Bekannte(n)** _bekunta_(n), OR (pal, mate) **der Kumpel(-)** _koompel_

friendly freundlich _froynd-likh_

frightened: to be frightened **Angst haben** _ungst-hahben_

from von [+ dat] _fon_, OR (as in "I come from Bonn") **aus** [+ dat] _aowss_, OR (with time/age, as in "from 6pm/13 years up") **ab** [+ dat] _up_

front: at/in the front **vorne** _forna_; in front of **vor** [+ acc or dat]² _for_

fruit das Obst _awpst_

full voll _fol_, OR (as in "I'm full") **satt** _zut_

fun der Spaß _shpahss_; it's fun **es macht Spaß** _ess mukht shpahss_; to have fun **sich amüsieren** _zikh amoohzeeren_; to make fun of **sich über** [+ acc] **lustig machen** _zikh oohber ... loosstikh mukhen_

funfair die Kirmes(sen) _keermes_(sen), OR **der Rummel** _roommel_

funny (amusing) **lustig** _loosstikh_, OR (odd, amusing) **komisch** _kawmish_

fuss: to make a fuss **Theater machen*** _tay-ahter mukhen_

2: If your sentence involves movement, use the accusative case; if not, use the dative. For more about cases, see p. 44.

gallery *die Galerie(n)* gullairee(yun)
game *das Spiel(e)* shpeel(a), OR (informal game of tennis, cards) *die Partie(n)* partee(yun)
garage (to get car mended) *die Werkstatt(¨en)* vairk-shtutt PL: vairk-shtetten (See also petrol station)
garden *der Garten(¨)* garten PL: gairten
garlic *der Knoblauch* k-nawblaowkh
gas *das Gas* gahss, OR (gasoline) *das Benzin* bentseen; gas station *die Tankstelle(n)* tunk-shtella(n)
gate (in airport) *der Flugsteig(e)* floog-shtyge(-a)
gear (car, bike) *der Gang* (¨e) gung PL: gheng-a
general *allgemein* ullga-mine
generous *großzügig* grawss-tsoog-ikh
geography *die Geographie* gai-aw-grufee
German *deutsch* doytsh, OR (man/woman) *Deutsche(n)* doytsha(n); in German *auf deutsch*
Germany *Deutschland* [n] doytsh-lunt
to get (buy) *kaufen* kaowfen, OR (fetch) *holen* hawlen, OR (obtain) *bekommen* bekommen, OR *kriegen** kreegun, OR (train/taxi) *nehmen* naimen, OR (understand) *mit'bekommen* mit-bekommen, OR *kapieren** kupeeren; to get away (escape) *entkommen* entkommen; to get off (bus, train) *aus'steigen aus* [+ dat] aowss-shtygen aowss; to get on (bus, train) *ein'steigen in* [+ acc] ine-shtygen in; to get along/on with (like) *sich verstehen* zikh fair-shtayun; to get up *auf'stehen* aowf-shtayun
girl *das Mädchen(-)* mait-khen
girlfriend *die Freundin(nen)* froyndin(nen)
to give *geben* gaiben, OR (as a gift, treat) *schenken* shenken (See also Verbs, p.45), OR (to pass) *reichen* rye-khen
glass *das Glas(¨er)* glass PL: glaizer
glasses (spectacles) *die Brille(n)* brilla(n)
glove *der Handschuh(e)* hunt-shoo(-a)
go: your go *du bist dran* doo bist drun; have a go! *versuch mal!* fairzookh-mahl; go-kart *der Go-Kart(s)* gaw-kart(s)
to go *gehen* gayen (See also Verbs, p.45); go! *los!* lawss
goal *das Tor(e)* tor(a)
god *der Gott(¨er)* got PL: gurter
good *gut* goot, OR (weather) *schön* shurn; good-looking *gutaussehend* goot-aowssayend; good morning *guten Morgen* gooten mawrgun; good afternoon *guten Tag* gooten tahg; good night *gute Nacht* goota nukht
goodbye *(auf) Wiedersehen* (aowf) veeder-zain, OR *tschüs** tshooss, OR (on the phone) *(auf) Wiederhören* (aowf) veeder-hur-un

gossip (scandal) *der Klatsch* klutsh
to gossip (natter) *schwätzen* shvetsen, OR (tell tales) *klatschen** klutshen
government *die Regierung(en)* rai-geeroong(en)
graffiti *Graffiti* [pl] grufeetee
gram *das Gramm(e)* grumm(a)
grandfather *der Großvater(¨)* grawss-fahter PL: grawss-faiter, OR (grandad) *Opa(s)* aw-pah(s)
grandmother *die Großmutter(¨)* grawss-mooter, OR (granny) *Oma(s)* aw-mah(s)
grant (for studies) *das Stipendium* shtippen-deeyoom PL: *Stipendien* shtippen-deeyen
grapefruit *die Pampelmuse(n)* pumpel-mooza(n), OR *die Grapefruit(s)*
grape *die Traube(n)* traowba(n)
grass *das Gras(¨er)* grass PL: graizer
grateful *dankbar* dunkbar
great (terrific) *großartig* grawss-artikh, OR *geil** guile
green *grün* groohn
grey *grau* graow
grilled *gegrillt* gegrillt
gross (horrid) *fies** feess
grotty (not very nice) *mies** meess
ground *der Boden* bawden; on the ground *auf dem Boden* aowf dem bawden; ground floor *das Erdgeschoß* aird-geshoss
group *die Gruppe(n)* grooppa(n)
to grow *wachsen* vuxen
to guess *raten* rahten
guest *der Gast(¨e)* gust PL: guesta; guest house *die Pension(en)* penzee-yawn(en)
guide *die Führer(-)*[1] foohrer
guilty *schuldig* shooldikh
guitar *die Gitarre(n)* giturra(n)
guy *der Typ(en)** toop(en), OR *der Kerl(e)** kairl(a)
gym (gymnasium) *die Turnhalle(n)* toorn-hulla(n); to do gym *turnen* toornen
gypsy *der Zigeuner(-)*[1] tsigoyner

habit *die Gewohnheit(en)* gavawn-hite(-en)
to haggle *feilschen* fileshen
hair *das Haar(e)* hahr(a) (See also picture opposite)
hairdresser (man) *der Friseur(e)* frizur(a), OR (woman) *die Friseuse(n)* frizurza(n)
hairstyle *die Frisur(en)* frizoor(en)
half *halb* hulp, OR (not whole, as in "half of it") *die Hälfte(n)* helfta(n)
ham *der Schinken(-)* shinken
hamburger *der Hamburger(-)* hum-boorger
hand *die Hand(¨e)* hunt PL: henda; handmade

1: If you are talking about a female, add *in* (**innen** in the plural). **2**: This word changes according to gender and case in the same way as *ein/eine*. See Articles, p. 44.

handgearbeitet <u>huntga-arbye-tet</u>; hands off!
Finger weg! <u>fing-er-vek</u>
to hang (something up) **auf'hängen** <u>aowf-hengen</u>; to hang around/out **sich herum'treiben** zikh hair<u>oom</u>-tryben; to hang up (phone) **auf'legen** <u>aowf</u>-laigun
hang-gliding **Drachenfliegen** [n] <u>drukhen-fleegun</u>
hangover **der Kater(-)** <u>kahter</u>
to happen **passieren** puss<u>ee</u>ren, OR **geschehen** ge<u>shay</u>en
happy **glücklich** <u>glook</u>likh
hard **hart** <u>hart</u>, OR (difficult) **schwer** <u>shvair</u>
hat **der Hut(¨e)** <u>hoot</u> PL: <u>hoo</u>-ta
to hate **hassen** <u>hussen</u>
to have **haben** <u>hahben</u> (See also Verbs p. 45); to have to **müssen** <u>moossen</u> (See Modal verbs p. 45)
hayfever **Heuschnupfen** [m] <u>hoy</u>-shnoopfen
he **er** <u>air</u>, OR **der*** <u>dair</u>
head **der Kopf(¨e)** <u>kopf</u> PL: <u>kurpfa</u> (See also to ache picture)
health **die Gesundheit** ga<u>zoont</u>-hite; health food shop **der Bioladen(¨)** <u>bee</u>-awl<u>ah</u>den PL: <u>bee</u>-awl<u>ai</u>den
healthy **gesund** ga<u>zoont</u>
to hear **hören** <u>hur</u>-un
heart **das Herz(en)** <u>hairts</u>(en); heartbroken **todunglücklich** <u>tawt</u>-<u>oon</u>-glook<u>likh</u>
heating **die Heizung** <u>hites</u>-oong
heavy **schwer** <u>shvair</u>
helicopter **der Hubschrauber(-)** <u>hoop</u>-shraowber
hell **die Hölle** <u>hur</u>la
hello **guten Tag** <u>gooten tahg</u>, OR **hallo*** <u>hullaw</u>
helmet **der Helm(e)** <u>helm</u>(a)
help **die Hilfe** <u>hilf</u>a

to help **helfen** [+ dat] <u>helfen</u>; to help yourself **sich bedienen** zikh ba<u>deenen</u>
her (as in her pen/book) **ihr²** [m, n] <u>eer</u>, OR **ihre²** [f, pl] <u>eera</u>
her (as in "he's taller than her" and "I can see her") **sie** <u>zee</u>, OR **die*** <u>dee</u>, OR (in dat. case) **ihr** <u>eer</u>, OR **der*** <u>dair</u> (For more about Cases, see p. 44)
here **hier** <u>heer</u>
hi **hallo*** <u>hullaw</u>
hiccups: to have hiccups **einen Schluckauf haben** <u>ine</u>-un <u>shlookaowf hahben</u>
to hide (something) **verstecken** fair<u>shteken</u>, OR (yourself) **sich verstecken** zikh fair<u>shteken</u>
hi-fi (system) **die Stereoanlage(n)** <u>shtairayaw-unlahga(n)</u>
high **hoch** <u>hawkh</u>
hiking: to go hiking **wandern gehen** <u>vundern gayen</u>
hill **der Hügel(-)** <u>hoohgul</u>
him **er** <u>air</u>, OR **der*** <u>dair</u>, OR (in acc. case) **ihn** <u>een</u>, OR **den*** <u>dain</u>, OR (in dat. case) **ihm** <u>eem</u>, OR **dem*** <u>daim</u> (For more about Cases, see p. 44)

hair **die Haare**

lockig <u>lokkikh</u>
glatt <u>glut</u>
kraus <u>kraow</u>ss
kurz <u>koorts</u>
schulterlang <u>shoolter-lung</u>
lang <u>lung</u>
rot <u>rawt</u>
blond <u>blont</u>
schwarz <u>shvarts</u>
braun <u>braown</u>

der Schaumfestiger <u>shaowm</u>festiger
der Fön <u>furn</u>
das Gel <u>gail</u>
der Haarspray <u>hahr</u>shpray
die Haarbürste <u>hahr</u>boohrsta
die Haarspange <u>hahr</u>shpunga
der Kamm <u>kum</u>

19

horoscope *das Horoskop*

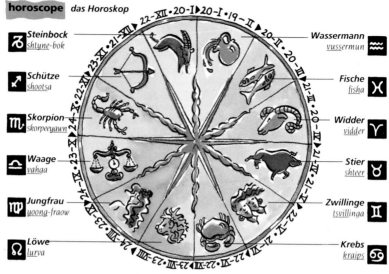

Steinbock *shtyne-bok*

Schütze *shootsa*

Skorpion *skorpeeyawn*

Waage *vahga*

Jungfrau *yoong-fraow*

Löwe *lurva*

Wassermann *vussermun*

Fische *fisha*

Widder *vidder*

Stier *shteer*

Zwillinge *tsvillinga*

Krebs *kraips*

Hindu (man/woman) *der/die Hindu(s)* *hindoo*(s)
hippy *der Hippie(s)* *hippee*(s)
his *sein*[1] [m, n] *zyne*, OR *seine*[1] [f, pl] *zyne-a*
history *Geschichte* [f] *geshikhta*
hit (success) *der Erfolg(e)* *airfolg*(a), OR *der Knüller(-)** *k-nooller*, OR (song) *der Hit(s)* *hit*(s)
to hit (strike) *schlagen* *shlahgun*, OR (hit target) *treffen* *treffen*
to hitch (a ride) *trampen* *trempen*
hitch-hiker *der Tramper(-)*[2] *tremper*
hobby *das Hobby(s)* *hobbee*(s)
to hold *halten* *hull-ten*
hole *das Loch("er)* *lokh* PL: *lurkher*
holiday *der Urlaub(e)* *oorlaowb*, OR (bank holiday) *der Feiertag(e)* *fire-tahg*; the holidays *die Ferien* *faireeyen*
Holland *Holland* [n] *hollunt*
home: at home *zu Hause* *tsoo haowza*; to go home *nach Hause gehen* *nakh haowza gayen*; home game *das Heimspiel(e)* *hime-shpeel*(a)
homeless *obdachlos* *obdukh-lawss*
homework *die Hausaufgaben* [pl] *haowss-aowf-gahben*
homosexual *homosexuell* *hawmaw-zexoo-el*
honest *ehrlich* *airlikh*
honey *der Honig* *hawnikh*
to hope *hoffen* *hoffen*
horn (of car) *die Hupe(n)* *hoopa*(n)
horoscope *das Horoskop(e)* *hawrawskawp*(a) (See also picture above)
horrible *furchtbar* *foorkht-bar*

horror film *der Horrorfilm(e)* *horrorfilm*(a)
horse *das Pferd(e)* *pfairt* PL: *pfairda*
hospital *das Krankenhaus("er)* *krunken-haowss* PL: *krunken-hoyzer*
host *der Gastgeber(-)* *gust-gaiber*
hostess *die Gastgeberin(nen)* *gust-gaiberin*(en)
hot *heiß* *hysse*, OR (spicy) *scharf* *sharf*; I am/feel hot *mir ist sehr warm* *meer isst zair vahrm*
hotel *das Hotel(s)* *hawtel*(s)
hour *die Stunde(n)* *shtoonda*(n)
house *das Haus("er)* *haowss* PL: *hoyzer*
hovercraft *das Hovercraft(s)* *hoverkruft*(s)
how *wie* *vee*; how are you? *wie geht's?* *vee gaits*; how much? *wieviel?* *veefeel*; how many? *wieviele?* *veefeela*
to hug (someone) *(jemanden) umarmen* *(yaymunden) oom-armen*
human *menschlich* *menshlikh*; human rights *die Menschenrechte* [pl] *menshen-rekhta*
humour *der Humor* *hoomawr*
hungry: to be hungry *Hunger haben* *hoong-er hahben*
hurry: to be in a hurry *es eilig haben* *ess eye-likh hahben*
to hurry *sich beeilen* *zikh ba-eye-len*
to hurt *weh tun* *vay toon* (See also to ache)
hypocritical *heuchlerisch* *hoykh-lerish*
hysterical *hysterisch* *hoostairish*
hysterics: to have hysterics (laughter) *sich tot'lachen** *zikh lawt-lukhen*

1: This word changes according to gender and case in the same way as *ein/eine*. See Articles, p. 44. **2**. If you are talking about a female, add *in* (*innen* in the plural). **3**: If your

I _ich_ <u>ikh</u>

ice _das Eis_ <u>ice</u>; ice cream _das Eis_ <u>ice</u>; ice cube _der Eiswürfel(-)_ <u>ice</u>-voohrfel; ice rink _die Eisbahn(en)_ <u>ice</u>-bahn(en)

idea _die Idee(n)_ ee<u>day</u>(en)

idiot _der Idiot(en)_ id-ee-<u>awt</u>(en), OR _der Dummkopf(¨e)*_ <u>doomm</u>-kopf PL: <u>doomm</u>-kurpfa

if _wenn_ <u>ven</u>, OR (stressed) _und wenn_ <u>oont</u> ven

ill _krank_ <u>krunk</u>

illegal _illegal_ illay<u>gahl</u>

imagination _die Phantasie_ fun-ta-<u>zee</u>

to imagine (to picture a situation) _sich vor'stellen_ zikh <u>forshtellen</u>, OR (as in "you're just imagining it") _sich ein'bilden_ zikh <u>ine</u>-bilden

immediately _sofort_ zaw<u>fort</u>

immigrant _der Einwanderer(-)²_ <u>ine</u>-vunderer

important _wichtig_ <u>vikh</u>tikh

in _in_ [+ dat or acc]³ <u>in</u>, OR (here) _da_ <u>dah</u> , OR (trendy) _in*_ <u>in</u>; in there (as in "it's in there") _da drin_ dah <u>drin</u>, OR (with motion, as in "go in there") _da rein*_ dah <u>rine</u>

to include _ein'schließen_ <u>ine</u>-shleessen

independent _unabhängig_ <u>oo</u>nup-heng-ikh

India _Indien_ [n] <u>in</u>deeyen

indoors _drinnen_ <u>drinnen</u>

infection _die Entzündung(en)_ ent-<u>tsoon</u>doong(en)

infectious _ansteckend_ <u>un</u>-shtekent

information _die Auskunft(¨e)_ <u>aow</u>sskoonft PL: <u>aow</u>sskoohnfta

injection _die Spritze(n)_ <u>shprit</u>sa(n)

injury _die Verletzung(en)_ fair<u>let</u>soong(en); injury time (in sports) _die Nachspielzeit_ nakh-shpeel-tsite

innocent _unschuldig_ <u>oon</u>shooldikh

insect _das Insekt(en)_ in<u>zekt</u>(en); insect bite _der Stich(e)_ <u>shtikh</u>(a); insect repellent _das Insektenschutzmittel(-)_ in<u>zekt</u>en-shoots-<u>mit</u>tel

inside (as in "it's inside") _drin*_ <u>drin</u>, OR (with motion, as in "come inside") _(he)rein_⁴ (hair)<u>rine</u>; inside out _links herum_ <u>links</u> hair<u>oom</u>

to insist on (something) _auf_ [+ dat] _bestehen_ aowf (...) be<u>shtay</u>en

instead _stattdessen_ shtut-<u>dessen</u>

instructor _der Lehrer(-)²_ <u>lair</u>er

instrument _das Instrument(e)_ instr<u>oomen</u>(a) (See also picture right)

insult _die Beleidigung(en)_ ba-<u>lye</u>-digoong(en)

insurance _die Versicherung(en)_ fair-<u>zikh</u>eroong(en)

intercom _die Sprechanlage(n)_ <u>shprekh</u>-unlahga(n)

interested: to be interested in _sich interessieren für_ [+ acc] zikh interes<u>seer</u>en foohr

interesting _interessant_ interes<u>sunt</u>

international _international_ intair-nutsee-<u>aw</u>nahl

interval _die Pause(n)_ <u>paow</u>-za(n)

interview (job) _das Vorstellungsgespräch(e)_ <u>for</u>shtelloongs-ge<u>shpraikh</u>(a), OR (with reporter) _das Interview(s)_ intair-<u>view</u>(s)

to introduce (people) _vor'stellen_ <u>for</u>-shtellen

invitation _die Einladung(en)_ <u>ine</u>-lahdoong(en)

to invite _ein'laden_ <u>ine</u>-lahden

Ireland _Irland_ [n] <u>eer</u>lunt

Irish _irisch_ <u>eer</u>ish, OR (man) _Ire(n)_ <u>eer</u>a(n), OR (woman) _Irin(nen)_ <u>eer</u>in(en)

iron (for clothes) _das Bügeleisen(-)_ <u>boohg</u>ul-eye-zen

island _die Insel(n)_ <u>in</u>zel(n)

instruments _Instrumente_

(See also **band** picture)

das Cello <u>tshel</u>law

die Geige <u>guy</u>-ga

der Flügel <u>floo</u>hgul

die Klarinette klari<u>netta</u>

das Horn <u>horr</u>n

die Trompete trom<u>pai</u>ta

die Oboe aw<u>baw</u>a

die Querflöte <u>kvair</u>-flurta

die Posaune paw<u>zaow</u>na

sentence involves movement, use the accusative case; if not, use the dative. For more about cases, see p. 44. **4**: In spoken German you often drop _he_.

it (when unclear what "it" refers to, as in "it's fine") **es** _ess_, OR **das*** _duss_, OR (when you know the gender of "it") **er¹** [m] _air_, OR **sie¹** [f] _zee_, OR **es¹** [n] _ess_, OR (slang) **der*** [m] _dair_, OR **die*** [f] _dee_, OR **das*** [n] _duss_; with it **damit** _dahmit_; on it **darauf** _dahraowf_; about it **darüber** _dahroohber_
Italy Italien [n] _itahleeyen_

jacket die Jacke(n) _yukka_(n), OR (bomber-style) **der Blouson(s)** _bloozong_(s) (See picture below left)
jam die Marmelade(n) marma-_lahda_(n), OR **die Konfitüre(n)** konfi_toohra_(n)
January Januar [m] _yanoo-ar_
jazz der Jazz _jazz_
jealous eifersüchtig _eye-fer-zookhtikh_
jeans die Jeans [pl] _jeens_
jellyfish die Qualle(n) _kvulla_(n)
jewellery der Schmuck _shmook_ (See picture below right)
Jewish jüdisch _yooh-dish_
job (employment) die Stelle(n) _shtella_(n), OR (task) die Arbeit(en) _ar-bite_(-en), OR **der Job(s)***
to jog joggen _joggen_
to join (become a member) **Mitglied werden** _mitgleed vairden_; to join in **mit'machen** _mit-mukhen_
joke der Witz(e) _vits_(a); for a joke **zum Spaß** tsoom _shpahss_
judo Judo [n] _yoodaw_
to juggle jonglieren _zhongleeren_

juice der Saft(¨e) _zuft_ PL: _zefta_
jukebox der Musikautomat(en) _moozeek-aowtawmaht_(en)
July Juli [m] _yoolee_
to jump springen _shpring-en_
June Juni [m] _yoonee_
junk der Trödel(-) _trurdel_; junk shop **der Trödelladen(¨)** _trurdellahden_ PL: _trurdelaiden_
just (as in "he's just gone" or "it's just right") **gerade** _garahda_

to keep behalten _behullten_; to keep on (doing something) **weiter'machen** _vyter-mukhen_; to keep an eye on **auf'passen auf** [+ acc] _aowf-pussen aowf_
key der Schlüssel(-) _shloossel_
kick der Tritt(e) _tritt_(a)
to kill töten _turten_; to kill yourself (laughing) **sich tot'lachen** zikh _tawt-lukhen_
kilo das Kilo(-) _keelaw_
kilometre der Kilometer(-) keelaw-_maiter_
kind (nice) **nett** _net_
kiss der Kuß _kooss_ PL: Küsse _koossa_
to kiss küssen _koossen_, OR (one another) **sich küssen** zikh _koossen_
kit (equipment) die Ausrüstung(en) _aowss-roosstoong_(en), OR **der Kram*** _krahm_
kitchen die Küche(n) _kookha_(n)
kite der Drachen(-) _drukhen_ (See also picture)
knee das Knie(-) k-_nee_(ya)
knickers der Slip(s) _slip_(s)

jacket die Jacke, OR der Blouson   **jewellery** Schmuck [m]

der Blouson
bloozong

der Kragen
krahgun

die Jacke _yukka_

der/das Revers
rayvair

der Ärmel
airmul

der Knopf
k-_nopf_

die Tasche
tusha

der Ohrring _or-ring_

die Kette _ketta_

die Halskette
huls-ketta

die Brosche
brosha

der Ring _ring_

die Schnalle
shnulla

der Armreifen
arm-_rye_-fen

das Armband
armbunt

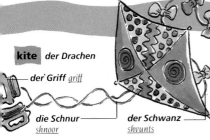

kite *der Drachen*

— *der Griff* <u>griff</u>

die Schnur — <u>shnoor</u>

der Schwanz <u>shvunts</u>

knife *das Messer(-)* <u>messer</u>
to know (facts) *wissen* <u>vissen</u> (See also Verbs, p. 45), OR (person, place) *kennen* <u>kennen</u>
kosher *koscher* <u>kaw-sher</u>

lager *das Pils(-)* <u>pils</u>, OR *das (helle) Bier(e)* (*hella*) <u>beer</u>(a) (For ordering, see beer and footnote 2, page 6)
laid-back *locker** <u>lokker</u>, OR *cool** <u>kool</u>
lake *der See(n)* <u>zay</u>(un)
lamb (meat) *das Lammfleisch* <u>lumm</u>-flyshe
land *das Land("er)* <u>lunt</u> PL: <u>lender</u>
language *die Sprache(n)* <u>shprah</u>-kha(n)
last (the last) *letzte(n)* <u>lets</u>-ta(n); at last *endlich* <u>entlikh</u>; last night *gestern abend* <u>gestern</u> <u>ahbent</u>
late (not early) *spät* <u>shpait</u>, OR (not on time) *verspätet* fair-<u>shpaitet</u>
to laugh *lachen* <u>lukhen</u>; to laugh at (a person, thing) *sich über* [+ acc] *lustig machen* zikh <u>oohber</u> (...) <u>loosstikh</u> mukhen; to burst out laughing *los'lachen* <u>lawss</u>-lukhen
launderette *der Waschsalon(s)* <u>vush</u>-<u>zullong</u>(s)
lazy *faul* <u>fowl</u>
leaf *das Blatt("er)* <u>blut</u> PL: <u>bletter</u>
to learn *lernen* <u>lairnen</u>
leather *das Leder(-)* <u>laider</u>
to leave *lassen* <u>lussen</u>, OR (a place/person) *verlassen* fair-<u>lussen</u>, OR (go away) *weg'gehen* <u>vek</u>-gayen
left (as in "the left(hand) side/shoe") *linke(n)* <u>linka</u>(n); on the left *links* <u>links</u>; left-handed *linkshändig* <u>links</u>-hendikh
leg *das Bein(e)* <u>byne</u>(-a)
leggings *die Leggings* [pl] <u>leggings</u>
lemon *die Zitrone(n)* tsi<u>trawna</u>(n)
to lend *leihen* <u>lye</u>-un, OR (money) *verleihen* fair-<u>lye</u>-un
leotard *das Trikot(s)* <u>treekaw</u>(s)
less *weniger* <u>vainiger</u>
lesson *die Stunde(n)* <u>shtoonda</u>(n)
letter *der Brief(e)* <u>breef</u>(a), OR (of alphabet) *der Buchstabe(n)* <u>bookh</u>-shtahba(n)
lettuce *der Kopfsalat(e)* kopf-zullaht(a), OR *der Salat(e)* zullaht(a)
liar *der Lügner(-)[2]* <u>loohg</u>-ner

library *die Bibliothek(en)* bibli-aw-<u>taik</u>(en)
licence (permit) *die Erlaubnis(se)* airlaowb-nis(sa); driving licence *der Führerschein(e)* <u>foohrer</u>-shyne(-a)
lie (fib) *die Lüge(n)* <u>looh</u>-ga(n)
life *das Leben(-)* <u>laiben</u>
lifeguard (at pool) *der Bademeister(-)[2]* <u>bahda</u>-my-ster, OR (on beach) *der Rettungsschwimmer(-)[2]* <u>rettoongs</u>-shvimmer
lifejacket *die Schwimmweste(n)* <u>shvim</u>-vesta(n)
lift (elevator) *der Lift(s)* <u>lift</u>(s), OR *der Fahrstuhl("e)* <u>farshtool</u> <u>farshtooh</u>-la
light *das Licht(er)* <u>likht</u>(er), OR (not dark) *hell* <u>hell</u>, OR (not heavy) *leicht* <u>lye</u>-kht
lighter *das Feuerzeug(e)* <u>foy</u>-er-tsoyg(a)
like *wie* <u>vee</u>; like this/that *so* <u>zaw</u>; what's he/she like? *wie ist er/sie?* vee <u>isst</u> air/zee
to like *mögen* [+ acc] <u>murgun</u> (See Modal verbs p. 45), OR *gern haben* [+ acc] <u>gairn</u> hahben, OR (to like doing something) *gern* <u>gairn</u> E.G. I like swimming *ich schwimme gern*; I'd like *ich möchte* ikh <u>murkhta</u>, OR *ich hätte gern* ikh <u>hetta</u> gairn
likely *wahrscheinlich* vahr-<u>shyne</u>-likh; not likely! *kommt nicht in Frage*!* kommt nikht in <u>frahga</u>
line *die Linie(n)* <u>lee</u>-nee-ya(n)
lip *die Lippe(n)* <u>lippa</u>(n)
to listen *zu'hören* <u>tsoo</u>-hur-un
litre *der/das Liter(-)* <u>leeter</u>
litter *der Abfall("e)* <u>upfal</u> PL: <u>upfella</u>
little (small) *klein* <u>klyne</u>; a little *ein wenig* ine <u>vainikh</u>
live (broadcast) *live* <u>live</u>
to live *leben* <u>laiben</u>, OR (dwell) *wohnen* <u>vawnen</u>
liver *die Leber* <u>laiber</u>
living room *das Wohnzimmer(-)* <u>vawn</u>-tsimmer
loads of *massenhaft* <u>mussen</u>-hufft
to loathe *verabscheuen* fair-<u>up</u>-shoyen
local *Orts~* <u>orts</u> E.G. local call *das Ortsgespräch*
to lock *ab'schließen* <u>up</u>shleessen
lonely *einsam* <u>ine</u>-zahm
long *lang* <u>lung</u>, OR (a long time) *lange* <u>lung</u>-a
loo *das Klo(s)** <u>klaw</u>(s) (See also toilet)
to look *schauen* <u>shaowen</u>, OR *gucken** <u>gooken</u>, OR (as in to look good/ill) *aus'sehen* <u>aowss</u>-zayen; to look after (care for) *auf'passen auf* [+ acc] <u>aowf</u>-pussen aowf; to look for *suchen* <u>zookhen</u>; to look forward to *sich freuen auf* [+ acc] zich <u>froyen</u> aowf; to look round (in shop, etc.) *sich um'sehen* zikh <u>oom</u>-zayen
to lose *verlieren* fair-<u>leeren</u>

1: In the accusative case, use *ihn* not *er*; in the dative, use *ihm* not *er* or *es*, and *ihr* not *sie*. For more about cases, see p. 44. 2: If you are talking about a female, add *in* (*innen* in the plural). **23**

lost *verloren* fair-_loren_; to get lost (on foot) **sich verlaufen** zikh fair-_laowfen_, OR (in car) **sich verfahren** zikh fair-_fahren_; get lost! **hau ab!** how _up_; lost property (office) **das Fundbüro(s)** _foond-boohraw_(s)

lot: a lot of **eine Menge** ine-a _meng_-a

loud *laut* _laowt_

lousy *lausig** _laow_-zikh, OR **fies*** _feess_

love *die Liebe* _leeba_; in love **verliebt** fair-_leept_; love-life **das Liebesleben** _leebus-laiben_

to love (doing something) *(...) sehr gern* (...) zair _gairn_, OR (someone) **lieb'haben** _leeb_-hahben, OR (adore) **lieben** _leeben_

lovely (beautiful) *schön* _shurn_, OR (nice) **lieb** leeb

low *niedrig* _needrikh_

low-down: to get the low-down **dahinter'kommen*** da-_hinter_-kommen

luck *das Glück* glook; bad luck! **Pech!** pekh; good luck! **viel Glück!** _feel_ glook

luckily *glücklicherweise* _glook_-likher-_vyze_-a, OR **zum Glück** tsoom _glook_

luggage *das Gepäck* _gepeck_; hand-luggage **das Handgepäck** _hunt_-gepeck

lunch *das Mittagessen(-)* _mittahg_-essen; to have lunch **zu Mittag essen** tsoo _mittahg_-essen

lyrics *der Text(e)* _text_(a)

machine *die Maschine(n)* mu_sheena_(n)

mad *verrückt* fair_rookt_, OR **wahnsinnig** _vahn_-zinnikh

magazine *die Zeitschrift(en)* _tsite_-shrift(en)

mail (letters) *die Post* _posst_

to make *machen* _mukhen_ (See also Verbs, p. 45); to make up (invent) **erfinden** air-_finden_, OR (be friends again) **sich versöhnen** zikh fair-_zurnen_

make-up *das Make-up* make-_up_ (See also picture opposite)

man *der Mann("er)* _mun_ PL: _menner_

to manage (cope) *zurecht'kommen* tsoo-_rekht_-kommen, OR (succeed) **es schaffen** ess _shuffen_

many *viele* _feela_

map *die Landkarte(n)* _lunt_-karta(n), OR (of town) **der Stadtplan("e)** _shtut_-plahn PL: _shtut_-plaina

March *März* [m] _mairts_

margarine *die Margarine* mar-gar_eena_

mark (German currency) *die Mark(-)* _mark_, OR (stain) **der Fleck(en)** _flek_(en), OR (at school) **die Note(n)** _nawta_(n)

market *der Markt("e)* _markt_ PL: _mairkta_

match (for a light) *das Streichholz("er)* _shtry-kh_-holts PL: _shtry-kh_-hurltser, OR (sport) **das Spiel(e)** _shpeel_(a), OR **das Match(e)** _metsh_(a)

material (cloth) *der Stoff(e)* _shtoff_(a)

maths *Mathe** [f] _mutta_

matter: it doesn't matter **es macht nichts** ess _mukht_ nikhts; what's the matter? **was ist (denn) los?** _vuss_ isst (den) _lawss_

mature *reif* _ryfe_

May *Mai* [m] _my_

mayonnaise *die Mayonnaise* my-on-_aiza_

me *ich* ikh, OR (in acc. case) **mich** mikh, OR (in dat. case) **mir** _meer_ (For more about **Cases**, see p. 44)

meal *das Essen(-)* _essen_

to mean (signify) *bedeuten* be_doyten_; to mean to **beabsichtigen** ba-_upzikhtigen_

meat *das Fleisch* _fly_-sh

medicine (medication) *das Medikament(e)* maydikah-_ment_(a), OR (science) **die Medizin** maydit_seen_

medium (size) *medium* may_deeyum_, OR **mittelgroß** _mittel_-grawss, OR (medium-cooked) **halbdurch** _hulp_-doorkh

to meet *treffen* _treffen_, OR (to get to know) **kennen'lernen** _kennen_-lairnen

melon *die Melone(n)* me_lawna_(n); watermelon **die Wassermelone(n)** _vusser_-melawna(n)

menu *die Speisekarte(n)* _shpyze_-a-karta(n), OR (a set menu) **das Menü(s)** men_oo_(s)

mess *das Durcheinander* _doorkhine_-under, OR (untidyness) **die Unordnung** _oonordnoong_

message *die Nachricht(en)* _nakh_-rikht(en); to take a message **etwas aus'richten** etvuss _aowss_-rikhten; to get the message **kapieren*** kup_eeren_

method *die Methode(n)* me_tawda_(n)

metre *der Meter(-)* _maiter_

microwave *die Mikrowelle(n)* _meekraw_-vella(n)

middle *die Mitte(n)* _mitta_(n)

midge *die Mücke(n)* _mooka_(n)

milk *die Milch* _milkh_; milk shake **der Milchshake(s)** _milkh_-shake(s)

mind: do you mind? (does it bother you?) *stört es dich/euch/Sie?[1]* _shturt_ ess dikh/oykh/zee; I don't mind (it doesn't bother me) **es stört mich nicht** ess _shturt_ mikh nikht, OR (it's all the same to me) **es ist mir egal** ess ist meer ay_gahl_

minute (time) *die Minute(n)* min_oota_(n)

mirror *der Spiegel(-)* _shpeegul_

Miss *Fräulein* _froy_-lyne

to miss (a bus/train) *verpassen* fair-_pus_-en, OR (to regret the absence of) **vermissen** fair-_missen_

mistake *der Fehler(-)* _failer_

to mix (a drink/medicine) *vermischen* fair-_mishen_, OR (to muddle) **durcheinander'bringen** doorkh-ine-_under_-bring-en

1: Use **Sie** to be polite, or informal **dich** with a friend and **euch** with several friends. **2**. If you are talking about a female, add **in** (**innen** in the plural).

mixed up (in your mind) *durcheinander* door-khyne-*under*

to moan (complain) *meckern** *meckern*

model (fashion) *das Mannequin(s) munna-kan(s)*, OR *das Model(s) model(s)*

modern *modern modairn*

moment in/just a moment! *Augenblick mal! aowgen-blik mahl*, OR **Moment mal!** *mawment mahl*; at the moment *momentan mawmentahn*

Monday *Montag* [m] *mawn-tahg*

money *das Geld ghelt*, OR *die Kohle(n)* kawla(n)*, OR *das Moos* mawss*

month *der Monat(e) maw-naht(a)*

most (most of all) *am meisten um my-sten*, OR (the majority of) *die meisten dee my-sten*

mother *die Mutter(¨) mooter*

motorbike *das Motorrad(¨er) mawtor-raht* PL: *mawtor-raider*

motorway *die Autobahn(en) aowtaw-bahn(en)*

mountain *der Berg(e) bairg(a)*

mouth *der Mund(¨er) moont* PL: *moonder*

to move *bewegen bevaigun*; to move house *um'ziehen oomtseeyen*; move over! *rück mal! rook mahl*

mooka(n), OR (in tropics) *der Moskito(s) mosskeetaw(s)*; mosquito bite *der Mückenstich(e) mooken-shtikh(a)*

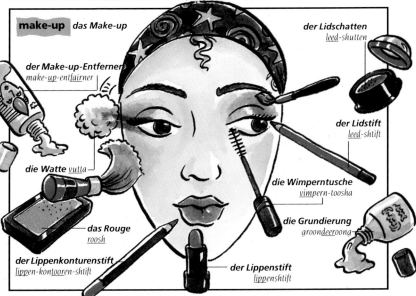

make-up *das Make-up*

der Lidschatten leed-shutten

der Make-up-Entferner make-up-entfairner

der Lidstift leed-shtift

die Watte vutta

die Wimperntusche vimpern-toosha

das Rouge roosh

die Grundierung groondeeroong

der Lippenkonturenstift lippen-kontooren-shtift

der Lippenstift lippenshtift

monument *das Denkmal(¨er) denk-mahl* PL: *denk-mailer*, OR (big) *das Monument(e) monooment(a)*

mood: in a good/bad mood *gut/schlecht gelaunt goot/shlekht galaownt*

moody (temperament) *launisch laownish*

moon *der Mond(e) mawnt* PL: *mawnda*

moped *das Moped(s) mawped(s)*, OR (small) *das Mofa(s) mawfah(s)*

more *mehr mair*, OR (additional) *noch mehr nokh mair*

morning *der Morgen(-) morgen*; in the morning *morgens morgens*

mosque *die Moschee(n) moshay(un)*

mosquito (in Europe) *die Mücke(n)*

movie *der Film(e) film(a)*

movies *das Kino(s) keenaw(s)*

Mr. *Herr hair*

Mrs. *Frau fraow*

much *viel feel*

mugged: to get mugged *überfallen werden oohber-falun vairden*

murder *der Mord(e) mort* PL: *morda*

muscle *der Muskel(n) moosskel(n)*

museum *das Museum moozayoom* PL: *Museen moozayen*

mushroom (button) *der Champignon(s) shompeen-yong(s)*, OR (field) *der Pilz(e) pilts(a)*

music *die Musik moozeek*

musician *der Musiker(-)[2] moozikker*

25

Muslim *moslemisch* moz<u>lai</u>mish
must (to have to) *müssen* <u>moo</u>ssen (See also Modal verbs p.45)
mustard *der Senf(e)* zenf(a)
my *mein*[1] [m, n] <u>mine</u>, OR *meine*[1] [f, pl] <u>mine</u>-a

naff *uncool** <u>oon</u>kool
naïve *naiv* ny-<u>eef</u>
naked *nackt* <u>nukt</u>
name *der Name(n)* <u>nah</u>ma(n); first name *der Vorname(n)* <u>for</u>-nahma(n); what's your name? *wie heißt du/ihr?*[2] vee <u>hye</u>-st doo/eer, OR *wie heißen Sie?*[2] vee <u>hye</u>-sen zee
napkin *die Serviette(n)* zairvee-<u>etta</u>(n)
narrow *eng* <u>eng</u>
nasty *unangenehm* <u>oon</u>ungenaim, OR (person) *gemein* ge-<u>myne</u>
national *national* nutsee-aw<u>nahl</u>
nationality *die Staatsangehörigkeit(en)* <u>shtahts-un</u>-gehurikh-kyte(en)
natural *natürlich* na<u>toohr</u>-likh
nature *die Natur* na<u>toor</u>
near *in der Nähe von* [+ dat] in dair <u>naya</u> fon
nearest (as in "the nearest shop/bank") *nächste(n)* <u>nexta</u>(n)
nearly *fast* <u>fust</u>
necessary *nötig* <u>nurtikh</u>
neck *der Hals(¨e)* <u>hults</u> PL: <u>heltsa</u>
to need *brauchen* <u>braowkhen</u>
needle *die Nadel(n)* <u>nahdel</u>(n)
negative *negativ* <u>naigateef</u>
neighbour *der Nachbar(n)*[3] <u>nakh</u>bar(n)
neighbourhood *die Gegend* <u>gaigunt</u>
nerve *der Nerv(en)* <u>nairf</u>(en); nerve-racking *nervtötend* <u>nairf</u>-turtent; what a nerve! *so eine Frechheit!* zaw ine-a <u>frekh-hyte</u>
nervous *nervös* <u>nairvurz</u>, OR (with excitement) *aufgeregt* <u>aowf</u>-geraikt
never *nie* <u>nee</u>; never mind! (it doesn't matter) *macht nichts!* <u>mukht</u> nikhts, OR (too bad) *ist doch egal!* isst dokh ay<u>gahl</u>
new *neu* <u>noy</u>; New Year *das neue Jahr* duss <u>noya</u> yar; New Year's Eve *Silvester* [n] zil<u>vester</u>; New Zealand *Neuseeland* [n] noy-<u>zaylunt</u>
news *die Nachrichten* [pl] <u>nukh</u>-rikhten; news stand (kiosk) *der Kiosk(e)* <u>keeosk</u>(a)
newsagent's (for papers) *der Zeitungshändler(-)* <u>tsye</u>-toongs-hendler
newspaper *die Zeitung(en)* <u>tsye</u>-toong(en)
next (as in "what/who is next") *am nächsten* um <u>nexten</u>, OR (as in "the next film/road") *nächste(n)* <u>nexta</u>(n); next to *neben* [+ acc or dat][4] <u>naiben</u>
nice (likeable) *nett* <u>net</u>, OR *sympathisch*

zoompahtish, OR (pretty) *hübsch* <u>hoopsh</u>; nice and ... (as in "nice and cold") *schön ... shurn ...*
nickname *der Spitzname(n)* <u>shpits</u>-nahma(n)
night *die Nacht(¨e)* <u>nukht</u> PL: <u>nekhta</u>; last night *gestern abend* <u>gesstern</u> <u>ahbent</u>
nightmare *der Alptraum(¨e)* <u>ulp</u>traowm PL: <u>ulptroyma</u>
no *nein* <u>nine</u>; no entry/smoking *Eintritt/Rauchen verboten* <u>ine</u>-trit/<u>raowkhen</u> fair-<u>baw</u>-ten; no way! *von wegen!** fon <u>vaygen</u> (See also not)
nobody *niemand* <u>neemunt</u>
noise *der Lärm* <u>lairm</u>, OR (din) *der Krach* <u>krukh</u>
normal *normal* nor-<u>mahl</u>
north *der Norden* <u>norden</u>; north of *nördlich von* [+ dat] <u>nurdlikh</u> fon
nose *die Nase(n)* <u>nahza</u>(n)
nosy *neugierig* <u>noy</u>gheerikh; to be nosy *die Nase in alles hinein'stecken** dee <u>nahza</u> in <u>ulless</u> hin<u>yne</u>-shtecken
not *nicht* <u>nikht</u>, OR (not a/any or no, as in "I've no money", "that's no joke") *kein*[1] [m, n] <u>kyne</u>, OR *keine*[1] [f, pl] <u>kyne</u>-a (See Negatives p. 45); not until *erst* <u>airst</u>
note (money) *der Schein(e)* <u>shyne</u>(-a)
notebook *das Notizheft(e)* naw<u>teets</u>-heft(a)
nothing *nichts* <u>nikhts</u>
novel *der Roman(e)* raw<u>mahn</u>(a)
November *November* [m] naw<u>vember</u>
now *jetzt* <u>yetst</u>; now then! *also!* <u>ulzaw</u>
nowhere *nirgends* <u>neerghents</u>
nuclear *Kern~* <u>kairn</u>, OR *Atom~* ut<u>tawm</u>, E.G. nuclear power *die Kernkraft*, OR *Atomkraft*
number *die Nummer(n)* <u>noomer</u>(n) (For numbers in German see p. 3)
nurse (man) *der Krankenpfleger(-)*

nuts *Nüsse*

die Cashewnuß keshoo-nooss

die Walnuß <u>vul</u>-nooss

die Kokosnuß kawkawss-nooss

die Pistazie pist<u>ahts</u>eeya

der Nußknacker <u>nooss</u>-k-<u>nucker</u>

1: This word changes according to gender and case, like *ein/eine*. See **2**: Use informal *du* (*ihr* in the plural), or polite *Sie* depending on who you talk to. See p. 44.
Articles p. 44.

krunken-pflaiger, OR (woman) _die_
Krankenschwester(n) _krunken-shvester(n)_
nut _die Nuß_ PL: _Nüsse_ _nooss_ (a) (See picture
below)
nuts: to be nuts (crazy) **spinnen*** _shpinnen_

obnoxious **widerlich** _veederlikh_
obscene **obszön** _obs-tsern_
obsessed **besessen** _bezessen_
obvious **offensichtlich** _offen-zikht-likh_
o'clock **Uhr** _oor_ (See picture for time)
October **Oktober** [m] _oktawber_
odd (strange) **eigenartig** _eye-genartikh_
of **von** [+ dat] _fon_, OR (made of) **aus** [+ dat] _aowss_
off (TV, light, machine) **aus(geschaltet)**
aowss(geshultet), OR (gas, electricity)
abgeschaltet _upgeshultet_
offended **beleidigt** _bel-eye-dikht_
to offer **an'bieten** _un-beeten_
office **das Büro(s)** _booh-raw(s)_
official **offiziell** _offitsee-ell_
often **oft** _oft_; how often? **wie oft?** _vee oft_
oil **das Öl(e)** _url(a)_
OK **in Ordnung** _in ordnoong_, OR **okay***, OR
(I'm/it's OK) **es geht** _ess gayt_
old **alt** _ult_; how old are you? **wie alt bist du?**[2]
vee ult bist doo, OR **... seid ihr?**[2] _... zyte eer_, OR **... sind
Sie?**[2] _... zind zee_; old-fashioned **altmodisch**
ult-mawdish, OR **passé** _pussay_, OR **out*** _aowt_
olive **die Olive(n)** _oleeva(n)_
omelette **das Omelett(s)** _om-let(s)_
on **auf** [+ acc or dat][4] _aowf_, OR (on an upright
surface, as in "on the wall/door") **an** [+ acc or
dat][4] _un_, OR (switched on) **an** _un_; what's on?
(TV, at the cinema) **was läuft?** _vuss loyft_

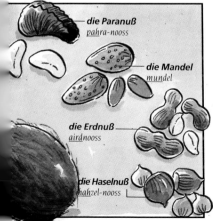

die Paranuß
pahra-nooss

die Mandel
mundel

die Erdnuß
airdnooss

die Haselnuß
hahzel-nooss

one-way: one way street _die_
Einbahnstraße(n) _ine-bahn-shtrahssa(n)_
onion **die Zwiebel(n)** _tsvee-bul(n)_
only **nur** _noor_, OR (with age or time, as in "he's
only 11", "only yesterday") **erst** _airst_; only child
das Einzelkind(er) _ine-tselkint_ PL: _ine-tselkinder_
open **offen** _offen_, OR **auf** _aowf_; in the open
air **im Freien** _im fry-en_
to open **öffnen** _urfnen_, OR **auf'machen**
aowf-mukhen
opera **die Oper(n)** _awper(n)_
opinion **die Meinung(en)** _mine-oong(en)_
opportunity **die Gelegenheit(en)**
galaigen-hyte(-en)
opposite (facing) **gegenüber** _gaigen-oohber_,
OR (not the same) **das Gegenteil(e)** _gaigen-tile(-a)_
optician **der Optiker(-)**[3] _op-tikker_
optimistic **optimistisch** _optimistish_
or **oder** _aw-der_
orange (colour) **orange** _orungsh_, OR (fruit)
die Orange(n) _orungsha(n)_
orchestra **das Orchester(-)** _orkester_
order (for food, drink) **die Bestellung(en)**
beshtelloong(en), OR (sequence) **die Reihenfolge**
rye-enfolga
to order (food, drink) **bestellen** _beshtellen_
ordinary **gewöhnlich** _gevurnlikh_
to organize **organisieren** _organeezeeren_
original **original** _origeenahl_, OR (person, idea)
originell _origeenell_, OR (earliest) **ursprünglich**
oor-shproong-likh
other (as in "the other shoe/side") **andere(n)**
undera(n)
otherwise **sonst** _zonst_
our **unser**[1] [m, n] _oonzer_, OR **unsere**[1] [f, pl] _oonzera_
out (not at home) **weg*** _vek_; to be out of
order (not working) **nicht funktionieren**
nikht foonk-tsee-yawn-eeren
outrageous **unerhört** _oon-air-hurt_
outside (with motion, as in "I'm going
outside") **nach draußen** _nakh draowssen_, OR
(without motion, as in "I'm outside") **draußen**
draowssen, OR (in front of, as in "outside the
cinema") **vor** [+ dat] _for_
oven **der (Back)ofen(¨)** _(buk)awfen_ PL: _(buk)urfen_
over (not under) **über** [+ acc or dat][4] _oohber_,
OR (as in "over here/there") **drüben** _droohben_,
OR (finished) **vorbei** _for-bye_; over the top
übertrieben _oohber-treeben_
overrated **überschätzt** _oohber-shetst_
to overtake **überholen** _oohber-hawlen_
to owe **schulden** _shoollden_
own: on your own **ganz allein** _gunts ull-ine_
owner **der Besitzer(-)**[3] _bezitser_

3: If you are talking about a female, add **in** (**innen** in the plural). **4**: If your sentence involves
movement, use the accusative case; if not use the dative. For more about cases, see p. 44.

to pack (bags) *ein·packen* *ine-pucken*
package tour *die Pauschalreise(n)* *paow-shahl-rye-za(n)*
padlock *das Vorhängeschloß* *forheng-a-shloss* PL: *Vorhängeschlösser* *forheng-a-shlursser*
page *die Seite(n)* *zyte-a(n)*
to paint (a picture) *malen* *mahlen*
palace *der Palast(¨e)* *pulusst* PL: *pulesta*
pan (saucepan) *der Topf(¨e)* *topf* PL: *turpfa*, OR (frying) *die (Brat)pfanne(n)* *(braht)-pfunna(n)*
panic *die Panik* *pahnik*
paper *das Papier* *pupeer*
paperback (book) *das Taschenbuch(¨er)* *tushenbookh* PL: *tushenbooh-kher*
parachute *der Fallschirm(e)* *fulsheerm(a)*
parcel *das Paket(e)* *pukait(a)*
pardon (what?) *wie bitte?* *vee bitta*
parents *die Eltern* [pl] *eltern*
park *der Park(s)* *park(s)*
to park *parken* *parken*
part (not all) *der Teil(e)* *tyle(-a)*, OR (for bike etc.) *das Teil(e)*; to take part *teil·nehmen* *tyle-naimen*
party *die Party(s)* *party(s)*, OR *die Fete(n)** *faita(n)*, OR (political) *die Partei(en)* *par-tye(-en)*
to party *feiern* *fye-ern*
pass (identity card, permit) *der Ausweis(e)* *aowss-vysse* PL: *aowss-vyze-a*; day pass (travel) *die Tageskarte(n)* *tahgus-karta(n)*; ski pass *der Skipass(¨e)* *shee-pus* PL: *shee-pessa*
to pass *vorbei·gehen an* [+ dat] *for-bye-gayen un ...*, OR (an exam) *bestehen* *beshtayen*
passenger (plane, ship) *der Passagier(e)* *pus-usheer(a)*, OR (train) *der/die Reisende(n)* *rye-zenda(n)*
passport *der Reisepaß* *rye-za-pus* PL: *Reisepässe* *rye-zapessa*, OR *der Paß* *pus* PL: *Pässe* *pessa*
pasta *die Nudeln* [pl] *noodeln*
path *der Weg(e)* *vaig(a)*
patient: to be patient *Geduld haben* *gedoold hahben*
pattern *das Muster(-)* *moosster*
pavement *der Bürgersteig(e)* *boohrger-shtyge(-a)*
to pay *bezahlen* *betsahlen*
pea *die Erbse(n)* *airbsa(n)*
peace *der Frieden* *freeden*
peaceful *friedlich* *freedlikh*
peach *der Pfirsich(e)* *pfeer-zikh(a)*
pear *die Birne(n)* *beer-na(n)*
pedestrian *der Fußgänger(-)*[1] *fooss-genger*; pedestrian crossing *der Fußgängerüberweg(e)* *foossgeng-er-oohbervaig(a)*

pen *der Stift(e)* *shtift(a)*, OR (ball-point) *der Kuli(s)* *koo-lee(s)*; pen pal *der Brieffreund(e)*[1] *breef-froynd(a)*
pencil *der Bleistift(e)* *blye-shtift(a)*
people *die Leute* [pl] *loyta*
pepper (vegetable) *die Paprikaschote(n)* *pupreekah-shawta(n)*, OR (spice) *der Pfeffer(-)* *pfeffer*
perfect *perfekt* *pairfekt*
performance (cinema) *die Vorstellung(en)* *forshtel-oong(en)*, OR (theatre) *die Aufführung(en)* *aowf-foohroong(en)*
perhaps *vielleicht* *fee-lye-kht*
period (menstruation) *die Tage** [pl] *tahga*, OR *die Periode(n)* *pairee·awda(n)*

phone booth *die Telefonzelle*

das Kartentelefon *karten-tailaifawn*
das Münztelefon *moonts-tailaifawn*
Notrufnummern *nawtroof-noommern*
der Hörer *hur-er*
das Fernsprechbuch *fairn-shprekh-bookh*
die Telefonkarte *tailaifawn-karta*

person *der Mensch(en)* *mensh(en)*
petrol *das Benzin* *bentseen*; lead-free petrol *das bleifreie Benzin* *blye-fry-a bentseen*; four-star petrol *das Super* *zooper*; petrol station *die Tankstelle(n)* *tunk-shtella(n)*
pharmacy *die Apotheke(n)* *up-awtayka(n)*
philosophy *die Philosophie* *filo-zawfee*
phobia *die Phobie(n)* *faw-beeya(n)*
phone *das Telefon(e)* *tailai-fawn(a)*; phone booth *die Telefonzelle(n)* *tailai-fawn-tsella(n)*; phone call *der Anruf(e)* *un-roof(a)*; long-distance phone call *das Ferngespräch(e)* *fairn-geshpraikh(a)* (See also picture above)
to phone (make a call) *telefonieren* *tailai-fawneeren*, OR (phone someone) *an·rufen* *un-roofen*
photo *das Foto(s)* *fawtaw(s)*
photographer *der Fotograf(en)*[1] *fawtaw-grahf(en)*

[1]: If you are talking about a female, add *in* (*innen* in the plural).

to pick (choose) *aus'wählen* <u>aowss</u>-vaylen, OR (gather) *pflücken* <u>pflook</u>en; to pick up (lift) *auf'heben* <u>aowf</u>-hayben

picnic *das Picknick(s)* <u>pik</u>-nik(s) (See also picture below)

picture *das Bild(er)* <u>bilt</u> PL: <u>bilder</u>

pie *die Pastete(n)* pus<u>tayta</u>(n)

piece *das Stück(e)* <u>shtook</u>(a)

pig *das Schwein(e)* <u>shvyne</u>(-a)

pill *die Tablette(n)* tub-<u>letta</u>(n), OR (contraceptive pill) *die (Antibaby)pille(n)* (untee-<u>baybee</u>)-<u>pilla</u>(n)

pinball *Flipper* [m] <u>flipper</u>

pineapple *die Ananas(-)* <u>un-un-us</u>

pink *rosa* <u>rawzah</u>

pity: it's a pity! *(wie) schade!* (vee) <u>shah</u>-da

pizza *die Pizza(s)* <u>peets</u>-ah(s)

place *der Ort(e)* <u>ort</u>(a), OR (seat) *der Platz(¨e)* <u>pluts</u> PL: <u>pletsa</u>, OR (position) *die Stelle(n)* <u>shtella</u>(n); at my place *bei mir* by <u>meer</u>

plan *der Plan(¨e)* <u>plahn</u> PL: <u>play</u>-na

plane (aircraft) *das Flugzeug(e)* <u>floog</u>-tsoyg(a)

plant *die Pflanze(n)* <u>pfluntsa</u>(n)

plaster (for cut or blister) *das Pflaster(-)* <u>pfluster</u>, OR (cast) *der Gips(e)* <u>gips</u>(a)

plastic *Plastik~* <u>plustik</u>, E.G. plastic bag *die Plastiktüte*

plate *der Teller(-)* <u>teller</u>

play (in theatre) *das Schauspiel(e)* <u>shaowshpeel</u>(a)

to play *spielen* <u>shpeelen</u>

player *der Spieler(-)[1]* <u>shpeeler</u>

please *bitte* <u>bitta</u>

plug (for water) *der Stöpsel(-)* <u>shturpsel</u>, OR (for electrics) *der Stecker(-)* <u>shtekker</u>

plum *die Pflaume(n)* <u>pflaow</u>-ma(n)

pocket *die Tasche(n)* <u>tusha</u>(n); pocket-money *das Taschengeld* <u>tushen</u>-ghelt

poem *das Gedicht(e)* ge<u>dikht</u>(a)

to point (to/at) *zeigen auf* [+ acc] <u>tsye</u>-gun aowf

Poland *Polen* [n] <u>pawlun</u>

police *die Polizei* polit-<u>sye</u>; police officer *der Polizist(en)[1]* polits-<u>isst</u>(en)

polite *höflich* <u>hurflikh</u>

politics *die Politik* poli<u>teek</u>

pollution *die Verschmutzung* fair-<u>shmoots</u>oong

poor *arm* <u>arm</u>

popular *beliebt* be<u>leept</u>

pork *das Schweinefleisch* <u>shvyne</u>-a-flyshe

positive (not negative) *positiv* <u>paw</u>-zit-eef, OR (sure) *völlig sicher* <u>furlikh</u> <u>sikher</u>

possible *möglich* <u>murg</u>-likh

post (letters) *die Post* <u>posst</u>; post-box *der Briefkasten(¨)* <u>breef</u>-kusten PL: <u>breef</u>-kesten; post office *die Post* <u>posst</u>, OR *das Postamt(¨er)* <u>posst</u>umt PL: <u>posst</u>emter

postcard *die Postkarte(n)* <u>posst</u>-karta(n)

poster (picture) *das Poster(-)* <u>pawster</u>, OR (advertising) *das Plakat(e)* plu<u>kaht</u>(e)

potato *die Kartoffel(n)* kar<u>toffel</u>(n); mashed potato *der Kartoffelbrei* kar<u>toffel</u>-brye, OR *das Kartoffelpüree* kar<u>toffel</u>-pooh-<u>ray</u>

pound (UK money) *das Pfund(-)* <u>pfoond</u>

practical *praktisch* <u>pruk</u>tish

to practise *üben* <u>ooh</u>-ben

picnic *das Picknick*

die Bank bunk

der Abfalleimer <u>upfal</u>-<u>eye</u>-mer

das Wasser <u>vusser</u>

das Brot <u>brawt</u>

das Frisbee® <u>frizbee</u>

der Käse <u>kayza</u>

die Wassermelone <u>vusser</u>-melawna

die Thermosflasche <u>tairmoss</u>-flusha

Trauben [pl] <u>traowben</u>

der Korb <u>korp</u>

die Küchenrolle <u>kookhen</u>-rolla

die Decke <u>dekka</u>

die Salami zal<u>ah</u>mee

das Taschenmesser <u>tushen</u>-messer

der Korkenzieher <u>korken</u>-tseeyer

die Kühltasche <u>koohl</u>-tusha

prawn (small) *die Krabbe(n)* <u>krubba</u>(n), OR (big) *die Garnele(n)* <u>garnayla</u>(n)

to prefer (something) *vor'ziehen* <u>for-tsee</u>-en, OR (doing something) *... lieber ... leeber*, E.G. I prefer painting *ich male lieber*

pregnant *schwanger* <u>shvunger</u>

to prepare *vor'bereiten* <u>for-berye</u>-ten

prescription *das Rezept(e)* ray-<u>tsept</u>(a)

present (gift) *das Geschenk(e)* ga<u>shenk</u>(a)

to press *drücken* <u>drooken</u>

to pretend *nur so tun* noor <u>zaw</u> toon, E.G. he's pretending *er tut nur so*

pretty *hübsch* <u>hoobsh</u>

price *der Preis(e)* <u>price</u> PL: <u>prye</u>-za

printer *der Drucker(-)* <u>drooker</u>

prison *das Gefängnis(se)* ga<u>fengnis</u>(sa), OR *der Knast** k-<u>nust</u>

private *privat* pree<u>vaht</u>

prize *der Preis(e)* <u>price</u> PL: <u>prye</u>-za

problem *das Problem(e)* praw-<u>blaim</u>(a)

programme *das Programm(e)* praw<u>grum</u>(a), OR (TV, radio) *die Sendung(en)* zen<u>doong</u>(en)

progress *der Fortschritt(e)* <u>fort</u>-shritt(a)

promise *das Versprechen(-)* fair-<u>shprekhen</u>

proof *der Beweis(e)* be<u>vice</u> PL: be<u>vyze</u>-a

prostitute (man) *der Strichjunge(n)* <u>strikh</u>-yoong-a(n), OR (woman) *die Prostituierte(n)* prostitoo-<u>eerta</u>(n)

Protestant *evangelisch* ayvun<u>gaylish</u>, OR *protestantisch* protes<u>tuntish</u>

proud *stolz* <u>shtollts</u>

psychological *psychologisch* psooh-khaw-<u>law</u>-gish, OR (in your mind) *psychisch* <u>psooh</u>-khish

pub *das Pub(s)* <u>pub</u>(s), OR *die Kneipe(n)* k-<u>nye</u>-pa(n)

public *öffentlich* <u>urfentlikh</u>

to pull *ziehen* <u>tseeyen</u>

puncture (flat tyre) *der Platten(-)* <u>plutten</u>

pure *rein* <u>ryne</u>

purpose: on purpose *absichtlich* <u>up</u>-sikhtlikh

purse *das Portemonnaie(s)* <u>port</u>-mon<u>nay</u>(s)

to push *schieben* <u>sheeben</u>

to put *stellen* <u>shtellen</u>, OR *tun** <u>toon</u> (See also Verbs p. 45), OR (in pocket/bag) *stecken* <u>shtekken</u>, OR (in lying position) *legen* <u>laigen</u>; to put away *weg'räumen* <u>vaig</u>-roymen; to put down *hin'stellen* <u>hin</u>-shtellen; to put off (postpone) *verschieben* fair-<u>sheeben</u>, OR (discourage) *ab'raten* <u>up</u>-rahten, OR (disgust) *an'ekeln* <u>un</u>-aykeln, OR (distract) *ab'lenken* <u>up</u>-lenken; to put on (clothes) *an'ziehen* <u>un</u>-tseeyen; to put up with *sich ab'finden mit* [+ dat] zikh <u>up</u>-finden mit

puzzle *das Rätsel(-)* <u>ray</u>-tsel, OR (jigsaw) *das Puzzle(s)* <u>puzzle</u>(s)

rain *der Regen*

der Regenbogen <u>raigun-bawgun</u>

der Regenschirm <u>raigun-sheerm</u>

die Pfütze <u>pfootsa</u>

der Regenmantel <u>raigun-muntel</u>

der Regentropfen <u>raigun-tropfen</u>

der Gummistiefel <u>goommee-shteefel</u>

quality *die Qualität(en)* kvuli<u>tayt</u>(en)

quantity *die Quantität(en)* kvunti<u>tayt</u>(en)

to quarrel *sich streiten* zikh <u>shtrye</u>-ten

quarter *das Viertel(-)* <u>feertel</u> (See also time)

question *die Frage(n)* <u>frah</u>-ga(n)

queue *die Schlange(n)* <u>shlung</u>-a(n)

quick *schnell* <u>shnell</u>

quiet (calm) *ruhig* <u>roo</u>-ikh, OR (not loud) *leise* <u>lye</u>-za; to be/keep quiet *still sein* <u>shtill</u> zyne; Quiet! *Ruhe!* <u>roo</u>-a

quite (fairly) *ziemlich* <u>tseem</u>-likh, OR (totally) *ganz* <u>gunts</u>

race *das Rennen(-)* <u>rennen</u>

racist *rassistisch* rus<u>sistish</u>

racket (tennis etc.) *der Schläger(-)* <u>shlayger</u>

radiator (in car) *der Kühler(-)* <u>koohler</u>

radio *das Radio(s)* <u>rahdee-aw</u>(s); radio cassette player *der (Radio)kassettenrecorder(-)* (<u>rahdee-aw</u>)kus<u>setten</u>-raykorder

raft *das Floß("e)* <u>floss</u> PL: <u>flurssa</u>

railway *die Eisenbahn(en)* <u>eye</u>-zun-bahn(en)

rain *der Regen* <u>raygun</u>; it's raining *es regnet* ess <u>raygnet</u> (See also picture above)

rape *die Vergewaltigung(en)* fair-ge<u>vultigoong</u>(en)

rare (uncommon) *selten* <u>zelten</u>, OR (steak) *blutig* <u>blootikh</u>

rash der Ausschlag(¨e) <u>aowss</u>-shlahg PL: <u>aowss</u>-
,shlayga
raspberry die Himbeere(n) <u>him</u>-baira(n)
raw roh <u>raw</u>
razor der Rasierer(-) ruz-<u>eerer</u>; razor blade
die Rasierklinge(n) ruz<u>eer</u>-kling-a(n)
reaction die Reaktion(en) ray-uktsee<u>yawn</u>(en)
to read lesen <u>layzen</u>, OR (aloud) vor'lesen
<u>for</u>-layzen
ready fertig <u>fair</u>tikh
real echt ekht
really (truly) wirklich <u>veer</u>-klikh, OR (extremely)
unheimlich* <u>oon</u>-hyme-likh
reason der Grund(¨e) <u>groont</u> PL: <u>groonda</u>
recently neulich <u>noy</u>likh
reception der Empfang(¨e) emp-<u>fung</u>
PL: emp-<u>fenga</u>
recipe das Rezept(e) ray-<u>tsept</u>(a)
to recognize erkennen air<u>kennen</u>
to recommend empfehlen emp-<u>failen</u>
record (music) die Schallplatte(n) <u>shull</u>-
plutta(n), OR (sport) der Rekord(e) ray-<u>kord</u>(a)
to record (tape) auf'nehmen <u>aowf</u>-naimen
red rot <u>rawt</u> (See also hair picture)
reduced (in sales) herabgesetzt hair-<u>up</u>-gazetst
to refuse ab'lehnen <u>up</u>-lainen
region die Region(en) rayghee-<u>awn</u>(en)
registered: by registered post per
Einschreiben pair ine-shrye-ben
regular regelmäßig <u>ray</u>gul-may-ssikh
rehearsal die Probe(n) <u>praw</u>-ba(n)
to relax sich entspannen zikh ent-<u>shpunnen</u>
relaxed entspannt ent-<u>shpunt</u>, OR locker* <u>locker</u>
relieved erleichtert air-<u>lye</u>-khtert

religion die Religion(en) rai-lighee-<u>awn</u>(en)
to remember sich erinnern an [+ acc]
zikh air-<u>innern</u> un
remote abgelegen <u>up</u>-galaigun; remote
control die Fernbedienung(en) <u>fairn</u>-
badeenoong(en)
to rent mieten <u>mee</u>-ten; for rent zu
vermieten tsoo fair-<u>mee</u>-ten
to repair reparieren raipah<u>reeren</u>
to repeat wiederholen veeder-<u>hawlen</u>
to reply antworten <u>unt</u>-vorten
research die Forschung <u>for</u>-shoong
reservation die Reservierung(en) raizair-
<u>veeroong</u>(en)
reserved reserviert raizair-<u>veert</u>
responsible verantwortlich fair<u>unt</u>-vortlikh
rest (break) die Pause(n) <u>paowza</u>(n), OR
(remainder) der Rest(e) <u>rest</u>(a)
restaurant das Restaurant(s) restaw<u>rung</u>(s)
result das Ergebnis(se) air-<u>gaybniss</u>(a)
return (ticket) hin und zurück <u>hin</u> oont tsoo<u>rook</u>
revenge die Rache <u>rukha</u>
to reverse (car) rückwärts fahren <u>rook</u>-vairts
fahren; to reverse the charges (phone) ein
R-Gespräch führen ine <u>air</u>-geshpraikh <u>foohren</u>
rice der Reis <u>rice</u>
rich reich <u>rye</u>-kh
rid: to get rid of (something)
[acc +] los'werden <u>lawss</u>-vairden
ride: to go for a (bike/car) ride eine Fahrt
(mit dem Fahrrad/Auto) machen ine-a <u>fart</u>
(mit daim <u>far</u>-raht/<u>aowtaw</u>) <u>mukhen</u>
ridiculous lächerlich <u>lekherlikh</u>
riding Reiten [n] <u>rye</u>-ten (See also picture below)

riding Reiten [n]

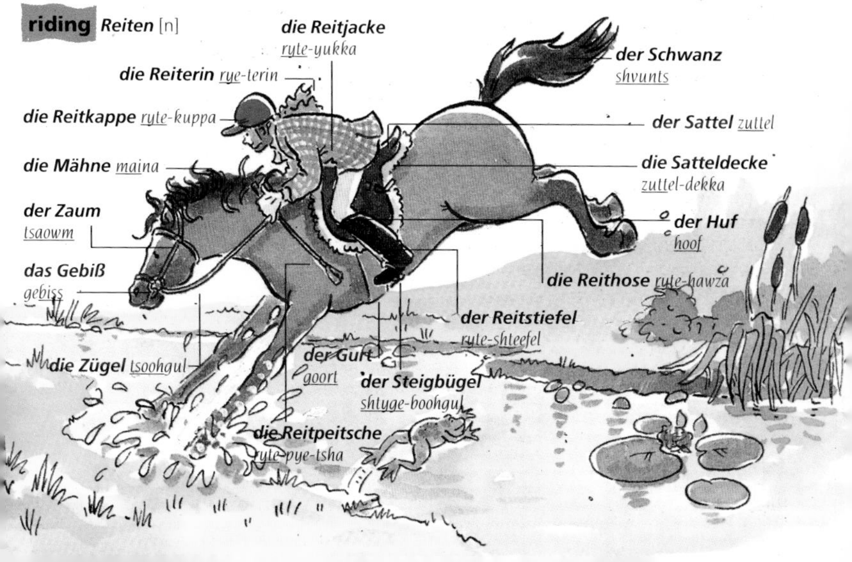

die Reitjacke <u>ryte</u>-yukka
die Reiterin <u>rye</u>-terin
die Reitkappe <u>ryte</u>-kuppa
die Mähne <u>maina</u>
der Zaum <u>tsaowm</u>
das Gebiß <u>gebiss</u>
die Zügel <u>tsoohgul</u>
die Reitpeitsche <u>ryte</u>-pye-tsha
der Gurt <u>goort</u>
der Steigbügel <u>shtyge</u>-boohgul
der Reitstiefel <u>ryte</u>-shteefel
die Reithose <u>ryte</u>-hawza
der Huf <u>hoof</u>
die Satteldecke <u>zuttel</u>-dekka
der Sattel <u>zuttel</u>
der Schwanz <u>shvunts</u>

right (as in "the right(hand) side/shoe")
rechte(n) <u>rekh</u>ta(n), OR (correct) **richtig** <u>rikh</u>-tikh;
to be right *recht haben* <u>rekht</u> hahben; that's
right *das stimmt* duss <u>shtimmt</u>; on the right
rechts <u>rekhts</u>; right-of-way **Vorfahrt** <u>for</u>-fart
riot *der Krawall(e)* kra-<u>vul</u>(a); to be a riot
(scream) *zum Schießen sein** tsoom <u>sheessen</u> zyne
to rip *reißen* <u>rye</u>-sen
ripe *reif* <u>rife</u>
rip-off: it's a rip-off! *so ein Nepp!** zaw ine nep
risk *das Risiko* <u>ree</u>-zikaw PL: **Risiken** <u>ree</u>-zikun
river *der Fluß* PL: **Flüsse** <u>flooss</u>(a), OR (large)
der Strom(¨e) <u>shtrawm</u> PL: <u>shtrurma</u>
road *die Straße(n)* <u>shtrahssa</u>(n); road map
die Straßenkarte(n) <u>shtrahssen</u>-karta(n)
rock (boulder) *der Felsbrocken(-)* <u>felz</u>-brokken,
OR (rock-face) *der Felsen(-)* <u>felzen</u>
roll (bread) *das Brötchen(-)* <u>brurt</u>-khen
romance (love affair/story) *die
Liebesgeschichte(n)* <u>leebess</u>-geshikhta(n)
romantic *romantisch* raw-<u>mun</u>-tish
roof *das Dach(¨er)* <u>dahkh</u> PL: <u>dekher</u>; roof rack
der Dachgepäckträger(-) <u>dahkh</u>gepeck-traiger
room *das Zimmer(-)* <u>tsimmer</u>; single/double
room *das Einzel~/Doppelzimmer* <u>ine</u>-tsel-/
<u>doppel</u>-tsimmer; twin room *das
Zweibettzimmer* <u>tsvye</u>-bet-tsimmer
rope *die Seil(e)* <u>zyle</u>(-a)
rotten (off) *verdorben* fair-<u>dorben</u>, OR (mean,
unfair) *gemein* ge-<u>mine</u>
round (shape) *rund* <u>roont</u>, OR (of drinks) *die
Runde(n)* <u>roonda</u>(n)
roundabout *der Kreisverkehr(e)* <u>kryse</u>-
fairkahr(a)
route *die Route(n)* <u>roota</u>(n), OR (bus) *die
Linie(n)* <u>leeneeya</u>(n)
to row (a boat) *rudern* <u>roodern</u>
rubber band *das Gummiband(¨er)*
<u>goomee</u>-bunt PL: <u>goomee</u>-bender
rubbish (litter) *der Abfall(¨e)* <u>upful</u> PL: <u>upfella</u>,
OR (garbage) *der Müll* <u>murl</u>; rubbish bin *der
Abfalleimer(-)* <u>upful-eye</u>-mer, OR *der
Mülleimer(-)* <u>murl-eye</u>-mer; to talk rubbish
*Quatsch reden** <u>kvutsh</u> raiden
rude *unhöflich* <u>oon</u>hurflikh, OR (crude) *grob*
<u>grawb</u>
rugby *Rugby* [n] <u>ruhgbee</u>
ruin *die Ruine(n)* roo-<u>eena</u>(n)
rule *die Regel(n)* <u>raigul</u>(n)
rumour *das Gerücht(e)* ge<u>rookht</u>(a)
to run *laufen* <u>laowfen</u>, OR *rennen* <u>rennen</u>; to
run away *weg'laufen* <u>vek</u>-laowfen; to run
out (expire) *ab'laufen* <u>up</u>-laowfen
rush hour *die Stoßzeit(en)* <u>shtawss</u>-tsyte(-en)

sad *traurig* <u>traow</u>-rikh
safe (out of danger) *sicher* <u>zikher</u>, OR (for
valuables) *der Safe(s)* <u>safe</u>(s)
safety *die Sicherheit* <u>zikher</u>-hyte; safety
belt *der Sicherheitsgurt(e)* <u>zikher</u>-hytes-goort;
safety pin *die Sicherheitsnadel(n)* <u>zikher</u>-
hytes-<u>nah</u>del(n)
sailing: sailing boat *das Segelboot(e)*
<u>zaigul</u>-bawt(a); to go sailing *segeln* <u>zaigeln</u>
(See also picture opposite)
salad *der Salat(e)* za<u>laht</u>(a); salad dressing
(French dressing) *die Vinaigrette* vinaig<u>rett</u>
salami *die Salami(s)* zu<u>lahmee</u>(s)
sale (reduced prices) *der Ausverkauf(¨e)*
<u>aowss</u>-fairkaowf PL: <u>aowss</u>-fairkoyfa; for sale *zum
Verkauf* tsoom fair-<u>kaowf</u>
salmon *der Lachs(e)* <u>lux</u>(a)
salt *das Salz(e)* <u>zults</u>(a)
same *derselbe*[1] [m] dair<u>zelba</u>, OR *dieselbe*[1] [f]
dee<u>zelba</u>, OR *dasselbe*[1] [n] dus<u>selba</u> , OR
dieselben [pl] dee<u>zelben</u>
sand *der Sand* <u>zunt</u>
sandwich *das Sandwich(es)* <u>zent</u>vitsh(es),
OR *das Brot(e)* <u>brawt</u>(a)
sanitary towel *die Damenbinde(n)*
<u>dahmen</u>-binda(n)
sarcastic *sarkastisch* zahr<u>kuss</u>tish
Saturday *Samstag* [m] <u>zums</u>-tahg, OR
Sonnabend [m] <u>zonn</u>-ahbent
sauce *die Soße(n)* <u>zawssa</u>(n)
sausage (large) *die Wurst(¨e)* <u>voorst</u> PL: <u>voorsta</u>,
OR (small) *das Würstchen(-)* <u>voohrst</u>-khen
to save (lives) *retten* <u>retten</u>, OR (money,
energy) *sparen* <u>shpahren</u>
savoury (not sweet) *nicht süß* <u>nikht</u> zoohss
to say *sagen* <u>zahg</u>-en
scared: to be scared (stiff) *(fürchterliche)
Angst haben* (<u>foohrkh</u>-terlikha) <u>ungst</u> hahben
scarf *der Schal(s)* <u>shahl</u>(s), OR (round neck)
das Halstuch(¨er) <u>hullts</u>-tookh PL: <u>hullts</u>-loohkher,
OR (round head) *das Kopftuch(¨er)* <u>kopf</u>-tookh
PL: <u>kopf</u>-toohkher
scary *gruslig* <u>groozlikh</u>
scenery (countryside) *die Landschaft(en)*
<u>lunt</u>-shufft(en)
school *die Schule(n)* <u>shoola</u>(n)
science *die Wissenschaft(en)* <u>vissen</u>-shufft(en)
scissors *die Schere(n)* <u>shaira</u>(n)
score (in a match) *der Spielstand* <u>shpeel</u>shtunt;
what's the score? *wie steht es?* vee <u>shtait</u> ess
Scotland *Schottland* [n] <u>shot</u>-lunt
Scottish *schottisch* <u>shottish</u>, OR (man)
Schotte(n) <u>shotta</u>(n), OR (woman) *Schottin(nen)*
<u>shottin</u>(en)

 1: This word changes according to gender and case, see **Articles**, p. 44.

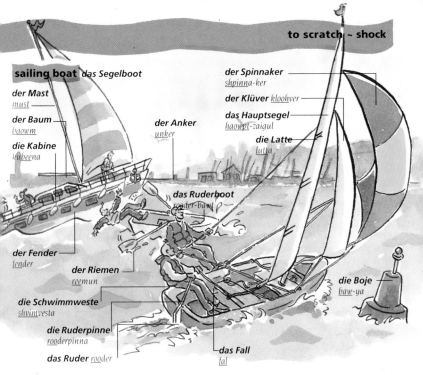

sailing boat *das Segelboot*

der Mast <u>must</u>

der Baum <u>baowm</u>

die Kabine <u>kabeena</u>

der Anker <u>unker</u>

das Ruderboot <u>rooder-bawt</u>

der Fender <u>fender</u>

der Riemen <u>reemun</u>

die Schwimmweste <u>shvimvesta</u>

die Ruderpinne <u>rooderpinna</u>

das Ruder <u>rooder</u>

der Spinnaker <u>shpinna</u>-ker

der Klüver <u>kloohver</u>

das Hauptsegel <u>haowpt</u>-zaigul

die Latte <u>lutta</u>

die Boje <u>baw</u>-ya

das Fall <u>fal</u>

to scratch *kratzen* <u>krutsen</u>

to scream *schreien* <u>shrye</u>-en

screen (cinema, movie) *die Leinwand* <u>lyne</u>-vunt, OR (TV, computer) *der Bildschirm(e)* <u>bilt</u>-sheerm(a)

scruffy *schlampig* <u>shlumpikh</u>

sculpture (object) *die Skulptur(en)* <u>skoollptoor</u>(en), OR (art) *die Bildhauerei* <u>bilt</u>-haowa-<u>rye</u>

sea *das Meer(e)* <u>mair</u>(a), OR *die See* <u>zay</u>

seafood *die Meeresfrüchte* [pl] <u>maires</u>-frookhta

seasick *seekrank* <u>zay</u>-krunk

season *die Jahreszeit(en)* <u>yahres</u>-tsyte(-en)

seat (place) *der Platz("e)* <u>pluts</u> PL: <u>pletsa</u>

second-hand *gebraucht* gaibraowkht

secret *das Geheimnis(se)* ga-<u>hyme</u>-niss(a)

secretary (man) *der Sekretär(e)* zekra-<u>tair</u>(a), OR (woman) *die Sekretärin(nen)* zekra-<u>tairin</u>(en)

to see *sehen* <u>zayen</u> (See also Verbs p. 45); to see again *wieder sehen* <u>veeder</u>-zayen; see you soon *bis bald* biss <u>bult</u>

to seem *scheinen* <u>shy</u>-nen

selfish *egoistisch* ego-<u>istish</u>

self-service *die Selbstbedienung* zelbst-<u>badeenoong</u>

to sell *verkaufen* fair-<u>kaowfen</u>

to send *schicken* <u>shikken</u>

sense *der Sinn(e)* <u>zinn</u>(a); it doesn't make

sense *es ist Unsinn* ess ist <u>oon</u>-zin; common sense *der Verstand* fair-<u>shtunt</u>

sensible *vernünftig* fair-<u>noonftikh</u>

sensitive *empfindlich* emp<u>fintlikh</u>

September *September* [m] zep<u>tember</u>

serious *ernst* <u>airnst</u>

service (in shop, restaurant) *die Bedienung* <u>badeenoong</u>

sex (gender) *das Geschlecht(er)* ge<u>shlekht</u>(er), OR (intercourse) *der Verkehr* fair<u>kair</u>, OR *der Sex** <u>zex</u>

sexist *sexistisch* zex<u>istish</u>

sexy *sexy** <u>zexee</u>

shade *der Schatten* <u>shutten</u>

shame: what a shame! *(wie) schade!* (vee) <u>shahda</u>

shampoo *das Shampoo(s)* shum<u>poo</u>(s)

shape *die Form(en)* <u>form</u>(en)

to share *teilen* <u>tyle</u>-en

shattered (tired) *erledigt* air-<u>lay</u>-dikht, OR (stunned) *platt** <u>plut</u>

to shave *sich rasieren* zikh ru<u>zeeren</u>

shaving foam *der Rasierschaum* ru<u>zeer</u>-shaowm

she *sie* <u>zee</u>, OR *die** <u>dee</u>

sheet *das Bettlaken(-)* <u>betlahken</u>

shirt *das Hemd(en)* <u>hemt</u> PL: <u>hemden</u>

shock *der Schock(s)* <u>shok</u>(s)

33

shoe *der Schuh(e)* <u>shoo</u>(-a); athletic shoes
die Trainingsschuhe [pl] <u>trainings</u>-<u>shoo</u>-a
shop *das Geschäft(e)* ge<u>sheft</u>(a), OR (small)
der Laden(¨) <u>lahden</u> PL: <u>layden</u>
shopping: to go shopping *einkaufen
gehen* <u>ine</u>-kaow<u>fen gayen</u>; window shopping
einen Schaufensterbummel machen <u>ine</u>-en
<u>shaow</u>-fenster-boommel mukhen
short *kurz* <u>koorts</u>; short cut *die
Abkürzung(en)* <u>up</u>-koohr-tsoong(en); short-
sighted *kurzsichtig* <u>koorts</u>-zikhtikh
shorts *die Shorts* [pl] <u>shorts</u>
shoulder *die Schulter(n)* <u>shoollter</u>(n)
to shout *schreien* <u>shrye</u>-en, OR (call out)
rufen <u>roofen</u>, OR (yell) *brüllen* <u>broollen</u>
to show *zeigen* <u>tsye</u>-gen; to show off
an'geben <u>un</u>-gaiben
shower *die Dusche(n)* <u>doosha</u>(n); to have a
shower *sich duschen* zikh <u>dooshen</u>
shut *geschlossen* ge<u>shlossen</u>, OR *zu* <u>tsoo</u>; shut
up! *halt den Mund!** <u>hult</u> dain <u>moont</u>
shy *schüchtern* <u>shookh</u>-tern
sick (ill) *krank* <u>krunk</u>; I feel sick *mir ist
schlecht* meer isst <u>shlekht</u>
side *die Seite(n)* <u>zyte</u>-a(n)
sightseeing *das Sightseeing* <u>syte</u>-seeing;
to go sightseeing *eine Besichtigungstour
machen* <u>ine</u>-a ba<u>zikh</u>-tigoongz-toor mukhen
sign (with hand etc.) *das Zeichen(-)* <u>tsye</u>-khen,
OR (on road etc.) *das Schild(er)* <u>shilt</u> PL: <u>shilder</u>
signature *die Unterschrift(en)* <u>oonter</u>-shrift(en)
Sikh (man/woman) *der/die Sikh(s)* <u>zeek</u>(s)
silent *still* <u>shtill</u>; to be silent (quiet) *still sein*
<u>shtill</u> zyne, OR (not to talk) *schweigen* <u>shvye</u>-gun
silly *albern* <u>ulbern</u>, OR *doof** <u>dawf</u>
simple *einfach* <u>ine</u>-fukh
since *seit* [+ dat] <u>zyte</u>, OR (since then)
seitdem zyte-<u>daim</u>
to sing *singen* <u>zing</u>-en
singer *der Sänger(-)*[1] <u>zeng</u>-er
single (not double) *Einzel~* <u>ine</u>-tsel E.G. a
single room *das Einzelzimmer*, OR (not return)
einfach <u>ine</u>-fukh, OR (record) *die Single(s)*
<u>zingel</u>(s), OR (unmarried) *ledig* <u>laidikh</u>
sister *die Schwester(n)* <u>shvesster</u>(n)
to sit (to sit down) *sich hin'setzen* zikh <u>hin</u>-
zetsen, OR (to be sitting down) *sitzen* <u>zitsen</u>
size *die Größe(n)* <u>grurssa</u>(n)
skate *der Schlittschuh(e)* <u>shlit</u>-shoo(a)
skating (on ice) *eis'laufen* <u>ice</u>-laowfen; roller
skating *Rollschuhlaufen* [n] <u>rolshoo</u>-laowfen
to ski *Ski laufen* <u>shee</u> laowfen
skiing *Skilaufen* [n] <u>shee</u>-laowfen; water-
skiing *Wasserskilaufen* [n] <u>vusser</u>-shee-laowfen;

ski resort *der Skiort(e)* <u>shee</u>-ort(a) (See also
picture opposite)
skin *die Haut* <u>haowt</u>
skirt *der Rock(¨e)* <u>rok</u> PL: <u>rooka</u>
sky *der Himmel(-)* <u>himmel</u>
slang *der Slang* <u>zleng</u>
to sleep *schlafen* <u>shlahfen</u>
sleeper (bunk) *der Schlafplatz(¨e)* <u>shlahf</u>-
pluts PL: <u>shlahf</u>-pletsa, OR (car) *der Schlafwagen(-)*
<u>shlahf</u>-vahgen
sleeping bag *der Schlafsack(¨e)* <u>shlahf</u>-zuk
PL: <u>shlahf</u>-zekka
slice *die Scheibe(n)* <u>shy</u>-ba(n)
to slip *aus'rutschen* <u>aowss</u>-rootshen
slob *der Schlamper(-)**[1] <u>shlumper</u>
Slovakia *Slowakische Republik* [f]
zlaw<u>vah</u>kisha raipoo<u>bleek</u>
slowly *langsam* <u>lung</u>-zum
small *klein* <u>klyne</u>
smart (cunning) *raffiniert* ruffee<u>neert</u>, OR
(elegant) *schick* <u>shik</u>
smell *der Geruch(¨e)* ge<u>rookh</u> PL: ge<u>rooh</u>-kha,
OR (good) *der Duft(¨e)* <u>dooft</u>(a), OR (bad) *der
Gestank* ge<u>shtunk</u>
to smell *riechen* <u>reekhen</u>
smile *das Lächeln* <u>lekheln</u>
to smoke *rauchen* <u>raowkhen</u>
smoking (sign) *Raucher* <u>raowkher</u>; non-
smoking *Nichtraucher* <u>nikht</u>-raowkher
snack bar *die Imbißstube(n)* <u>imbiss</u>-shtooba(n)
snake *die Schlange(n)* <u>shlung</u>-a(n)
sneaky (cunning) *raffiniert* ruffee<u>neert</u>
to sneeze *niesen* <u>neezen</u>
snooty *hochnäsig* <u>hawkh</u>-naizikh
snow *der Schnee* <u>shnai</u> (See also weather)
so (as in "it's so easy") *so* <u>zaw</u>, OR (as in "so,
be quick") *also* <u>ulzaw</u>; so-so (not great) *soso*
zaw-<u>zaw</u>; so what? *na und?* na-<u>oont</u>
soap *die Seife(n)* <u>zye</u>-fa(n); soap opera *die
Serie(n)* <u>zaireeya</u>(n), OR *die Soap(s)** <u>zoap</u>(s)
soccer (football) *Fußball* [m] <u>foossbul</u> (See
also football)
society *die Gesellschaft(en)* ge<u>zell</u>-shufft(en)
sock *die Socke(n)* <u>zokka</u>(n)
soft *weich* <u>vye-kh</u>; soft drink *das alkoholfreie
Getränk* <u>ulkawhawl</u>-<u>fry</u>-a getrenk
software *die Software(s)* <u>zoft</u>-vair(s)
soldier *der Soldat(en)*[1] zol-<u>daht</u>(en)
some (a few) *einige* <u>ine</u>-iga, OR (certain, as in
"some people") *manche* <u>muncha</u>
somebody *jemand* <u>yaimunt</u>; somebody
else *jemand anders* <u>yaimunt</u> <u>unders</u>
something *etwas* <u>etvuss</u>; something else
etwas anderes etvuss <u>underes</u>

1: If you are talking about a female, add *in* (*innen* in the plural).

sometimes *manchmal* <u>munch-mahl</u>
somewhere *irgendwo* <u>eer-ghent-vaw</u>;
somewhere else **woanders** <u>vaw-unders</u>
song *das Lied(er)* <u>leet</u> PL: <u>leeder</u>
soon *bald* <u>bult</u>
sorry (forgive me) *Verzeihung* <u>fair-tsye-oong</u>;
I'm sorry **es tut mir leid** *ess <u>toot</u> meer <u>lyte</u>*
sort *die Art(en)* <u>art</u>(en), OR *die Sorte(n)* <u>zorta</u>(n)
sound *der Laut(e)* <u>laowt</u>(a), OR (noise) *das
Geräusch(e)* <u>geroysh</u>(a), OR (musical) *der
Klang(¨e)* <u>klung</u> PL: <u>kleng-a</u>, OR (T.V., stereo) *der
Ton(¨e)* <u>tawn</u> PL: <u>turna</u>
soup *die Suppe(n)* <u>zooppa</u>(n)
south *der Süden* <u>zoohden</u>; south of **südlich
von** [+ dat] <u>zoohdlikh fon</u>
souvenir *das Souvenir(s)* <u>zoo-veneer</u>(s)
space (room) *der Platz* <u>pluts</u>, OR (outer space)
der Weltraum <u>velt-raowm</u>
Spain *Spanien* [n] <u>shpahneeyen</u>
spare *übrig* <u>oohbrikh</u>; spare part *das
Ersatzteil(e)* <u>airzuts-tyle</u>; spare time *die
Freizeit* <u>fry-tsyte</u>
to speak *sprechen* <u>shprekhen</u>
speaker (loudspeaker) *der Lautsprecher(-)*
<u>laowt-shprekher</u>, OR (with hi-fi) *die Box(en)* <u>box</u>(en)
speciality *die Spezialität(en)* <u>shpetsee-ulitait</u>(en)
speed *das Tempo* <u>tempaw</u>; at full speed
mit vollem Tempo *mit <u>follem</u> <u>tempaw</u>*
to spend (money) *aus'geben* <u>owss-gaiben</u>,
OR (time) *verbringen* <u>fair-bring-en</u>
spice *das Gewürz(e)* <u>gevoohrts</u>(a)

skiing *Skilaufen* [n]

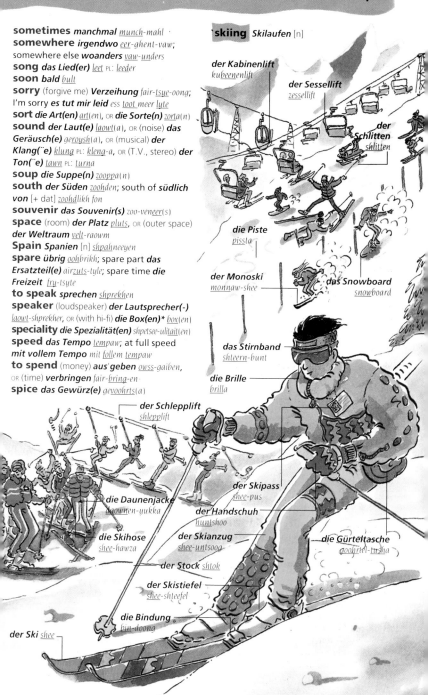

der Kabinenlift
<u>kubeenenlift</u>

der Sessellift
<u>zessellift</u>

der Schlitten
<u>shlitten</u>

die Piste
<u>pissta</u>

der Monoski
<u>monnaw-shee</u>

das Snowboard
<u>snowboard</u>

das Stirnband
<u>shteern-bunt</u>

die Brille
<u>brilla</u>

der Schlepplift
<u>shlepplift</u>

die Daunenjacke
<u>daownen-yukka</u>

die Skihose
<u>shee-hawza</u>

der Skipass
<u>shee-pus</u>

der Handschuh
<u>huntshoo</u>

der Skianzug
<u>shee-untsoog</u>

die Gürteltasche
<u>goohrtel-tasha</u>

der Stock <u>shtok</u>

der Skistiefel
<u>shee-shteefel</u>

die Bindung
<u>bin-doong</u>

der Ski <u>shee</u>

spicy *würzig* <u>voohrtsikh</u>
spider *die Spinne(n)* <u>shpinna</u>(n)
spinach *der Spinat* shpin<u>aht</u>
to spit *spucken* <u>shpooken</u>
to split (share out) *auf'teilen* <u>owf</u>-tyle-en, OR
(leave) *ab'hauen* <u>up</u>-haowen; to split up
(relationship) *sich trennen* zikh <u>trennen</u>
to spoil (ruin) *verderben* <u>fair</u>-dairben, OR (to
damage) *beschädigen* beshai-digen.
spoiled (child) *verwöhnt* fair-<u>vurnt</u>
spontaneous *spontan* shpon-<u>tahn</u>
spoon *der Löffel(-)* <u>lurfel</u>
sport *der Sport* <u>shport</u>; sports centre *das
Sportzentrum* <u>shport</u>-<u>tsent</u>room PL: *Sportzentren*
<u>shport</u>-<u>tsent</u>ren
sporty (athletic) *sportlich* <u>shport</u>likh
spot (pimple) *der Pickel(-)* <u>pickel</u>, OR (place)
die Stelle(n) <u>shtella</u>(n)
sprain (wrist/ankle) *die Verstauchung(en)*
fair-<u>shtaowkh</u>-oong(en)
spring (season) *der Frühling* <u>froohling</u>, OR
(water) *die Quelle(n)* <u>kvella</u>(n)
spy (man) *der Spion(e)* shpee-<u>yawn</u>(a), OR
(woman) *die Spionin(nen)* shpee-<u>yawn</u>in(en)
square (in town) *der Platz('e)* <u>pluts</u> PL: <u>pletsa</u>
squash (game) *Squash* [n] <u>skvosh</u>
stairs *die Treppe(n)* <u>treppa</u>(n)
stamp *die Briefmarke(n)* <u>breef</u>-marka(n)
to stand (not sit) *stehen* <u>shtayen</u>, OR (bear)
aus'stehen <u>aowss</u>-shtayen, E.G. I can't stand...
ich kann ... nicht ausstehen; to stand up for
verteidigen fair-<u>tye</u>-digen
stand-by *Standby~* <u>stend</u>-bye E.G. stand-by
ticket *das Standby-Ticket(s)*
star (in sky) *der Stern(e)* <u>shtairn</u>(a), OR (man/
woman in film/movie) *der Star(s)* <u>star</u>(s)
start *der Anfang('e)* <u>unfung</u> PL: <u>unfeng</u>-a, OR
(of race) *der Start(s)* <u>shtart</u>(s)
starter (first course) *die Vorspeise(n)* for-
<u>shpye</u>-za(n)
station (train) *der Bahnhof('e)* <u>bahn</u>-hawf
PL: <u>bahn</u>-hurfa, OR (underground) *die Station(en)*
<u>shtuts</u>-yawn(en), OR (radio) *der Sender(-)* <u>zender</u>
statue *die Statue(n)* <u>shtah</u>too-a(n)
to stay (remain) *bleiben* <u>blye</u>-ben, OR
(overnight) *übernachten* oober-<u>nukh</u>ten, OR
(several nights) *wohnen* <u>vawnen</u>
steak *das Steak(s)* <u>shtaik</u>(s)
to steal *stehlen* <u>shtailen</u>
steep *steil* <u>shtyle</u>
step (footstep) *der Schritt(e)* <u>shritt</u>(a), OR
(stair) *die Stufe(n)* <u>shtoofa</u>(n)
stereo (hi-fi system) *die Stereoanlage(n)*
<u>shtairayaw</u>-<u>unlahga</u>(n)

stereotyped *stereotyp* <u>shtairayaw</u>-toop
stiff *steif* <u>shtyfe</u>
still (even now) *noch* <u>nokh</u>, OR (stressed as in
"he's <u>still</u> there") *immer noch* <u>immer</u>-nokh
to sting (insect) *stechen* <u>shtekhen</u>, OR (jelly
fish, nettles) *verbrennen* fair-<u>brennen</u>
stingy (not generous) *geizig* <u>guy</u>-tsikh
to stink *stinken* <u>shtinken</u>
to stir (cooking) *um'rühren* <u>oom</u>-roohren, OR
(cause trouble) *auf'hetzen* <u>aowf</u>-hetsen
stomach *der Magen(¨)* <u>mahgen</u> PL: <u>maigen</u>,
OR (tummy) *der Bauch('e)* <u>baowkh</u> PL: <u>boykha</u>;
upset stomach *die Magenverstimmung(en)*
<u>mahgen</u>-fair-<u>shtimmoong</u>(en) (See also ache picture)
stone *der Stein(e)* <u>shtyne</u>(a)
to stop (doing something) *auf'hören* <u>aowf</u>-
hur-en, OR (come to a halt) *an'halten* <u>un</u>-hulten,
OR (prevent) *verhindern* fair-<u>hindern</u>
stopover (plane) *die Zwischenlandung(en)*
<u>tsvishen</u>-lundoong(en)
storm *der Sturm(¨e)* <u>shtoorm</u> PL: <u>shtoohrma</u>,
OR (with lightning) *das Gewitter(-)* ge<u>vitter</u>
story *die Geschichte(n)* ge<u>shikhta</u>(n), OR
(plot) *die Handlung(en)* <u>huntloong</u>(en), OR (in
newspaper) *der Artikel(-)* ar<u>teekel</u>
straight (not curved) *gerade* ge<u>rahda</u>, OR
(directly) *direkt* dee<u>rekt</u>, OR (a bit square)
konventionell konventsee-aw<u>nell</u>; straight
ahead *geradeaus* ge<u>rahda</u>-aowss; straight
away *sofort* zaw<u>fort</u>
strange *seltsam* <u>zelt</u>-zahm
strawberry *die Erdbeere(n)* <u>aird</u>-baira(n)
street *die Straße(n)* <u>shtrahssa</u>(n)
stress *der Streß* <u>shtress</u>

to sunbathe *sich sonnen*

der Sonnenschirm <u>zonnen</u>-sheerm

das Badetuch <u>bahda</u>-tookh

die Sonnenbrille <u>zonnen</u>-brilla

die Sonnencreme <u>zonnen</u>-kraim

strict *streng* shtreng
strike *der Streik(s)* shtryke
string *die Schnur("e)* shnoor PL: shnoohra
striped *gestreift* geshtrye-ft
strong *stark* shtark
stubborn *stur* shtoor
stuck-up *eingebildet* ine-gebildet
student (man) *der Student(en)* shtoodent(en), OR (woman) *die Studentin(nen)* shtoodentin(en)
to study *studieren* shtoodeeren
stuff *das Zeug* tsoyg, OR *der Kram** krahm
stuffy (no air) *stickig* shtickikh, OR (straight, old-fashioned) *verstaubt* fairshtaowbt
stunning (amazing) *verblüffend* fair-blooffent, OR (gorgeous, terrific) *toll** toll
stupid *dumm* doomm, OR *blöd** blurd
style *der Stil(e)* shteel(a)
subconsciously *im Unterbewußtsein* im oonter-bevoosst-zyne
subject *das Thema* taimah PL: *Themen* taimen, OR (at school) *das Fach("er)* fukh PL: fekher
subtitle *der Untertitel(-)* oonter-teetel
suburbs *der Vorort(e)* for-ort(a); in the suburbs *am Stadtrand* um shtutrunt
to succeed *Erfolg haben* airfolg hahben
success *der Erfolg(e)* airfolg(a)
suddenly *plötzlich* plurtslikh
to suffer *leiden* lye-den
sugar *der Zucker* tsooker
to suggest *vor'schlagen* for-shlahgen
suit *der Anzug("e)* untsoog PL: untsooga
to suit: it suits you *es steht dir gut* ess shtait deer goot
suitcase *der Koffer(-)* koffer
summer *der Sommer(-)* zommer
sun *die Sonne(n)* zonna(n); sun block *der Sonnenblock(s)* zonnen-block(s); sun cream *die Sonnencreme(s)* zonnen-kraim(s)

to sunbathe *sich sonnen* zikh zonnen (See also picture below left)
sunburned *sonnenverbrannt* zonnen-fairbrunt
Sunday *Sonntag* [m] zonntahg
sunglasses *die Sonnenbrille(n)* zonnen-brilla(n)
sunny *sonnig* zonnikh
sunset *der Sonnenuntergang("e)* zonnen-oontergung PL: zonnen-oontergenga
sunstroke *der Sonnenstich* zonnen-shtikh
superficial *oberflächlich* awber-flekhlikh
supermarket *der Supermarkt("e)* zoopermarkt PL: zoopermairkta
superstitious *abergläubisch* ahbergloybish
supper (meal) *das Abendessen(-)* ahbent-essen
supplement *der Zuschlag("e)* tsooshlahg PL: tsooshlayga
to suppose *an'nehmen* un-naimen
supposed: to be supposed to *sollen* zollen (See also Modal verbs p. 45)
sure *sicher* zikher
to surf *surfen* zoorfen (See also picture below)
surprise *die Überraschung(en)* oohber-rushoong(en)
suspense *die Spannung* shpunnoong
to swallow *schlucken* shlooken
to swap *tauschen* taowshen
to swear (promise) *schwören* shvuren, OR (say bad words) *fluchen* flookhen
swearword *das Schimpfwort("er)* shimfvort PL: shimfvurter
to sweat *schwitzen* shvitsen
sweater *der Pullover(-)* pull-awver, OR *der Pulli(s)** poolee(s)
sweatshirt *das Sweatshirt(s)* svet-shurt(s)
sweet (candy) *die Süßigkeit(en)* zoohssikh-kyte(-en), OR (sugary, cute) *süß* zoohss

die Düne doohna
der Windschutz vint-shoots
to surf *surfen*
das Meer mair
der Sand zunt
die Sonnenliege zonnen-leega
die Welle vella
der Liegestuhl leega-shtool
das Surfbrett zoorf-brett
die Luftmatratze looft-mutrutsa
der Sonnenhut zonnenhoot
der Surfer zoorfer

to swim *schwimmen* <u>shvimmen</u> (See also picture below)

swimming *Schwimmen* [n] <u>shvimmen</u>; swimming pool *das Schwimmbad("er)* <u>shvimmbaht</u> PL: <u>shvimmbayder</u>

Switzerland *die Schweiz* <u>shvye-ts</u>

swollen *geschwollen* <u>geshvollen</u>

synagogue *die Synagoge(n)* <u>zoona-gawga</u>(n)

table *der Tisch(e)* <u>tish</u>(a); table football *Tischfußball* [m] <u>tishfooss-bul</u>; table tennis *Ping-pong** [n] <u>ping-pong</u>, OR *Tischtennis* [n] <u>tish-tennis</u>

to take *nehmen* <u>naimen</u> (See also Verbs p. 45), OR (to accompany) *bringen* <u>bring-en</u>; to take away *weg'nehmen* <u>vaig-naimen</u>, OR (food) *mit'nehmen* <u>mit-naimen</u>; to take off (clothes) *aus'ziehen* <u>owss-tseeyen</u>

to talk *sprechen* <u>shprekhen</u>

tall *groß* <u>grawss</u>

tampon *der Tampon(s)* <u>tumpon</u>(s)

tanned *braun* <u>brown</u>

tap *der Wasserhahn("e)* <u>vusser-hahn</u> PL: <u>vusser-haina</u>

tape (cassette) *die Kassette(n)* <u>kussetta</u>(n)

tart *die Torte(n)* <u>torta</u>(n), OR *der Kuchen(-)* <u>kookhen</u>, OR (small) *das Törtchen(-)* <u>turtkhen</u>

taste *der Geschmack("e)* <u>geshmuk</u> PL: <u>geshmekka</u>

to taste (as in "taste it") *probieren* <u>probeeren</u>, OR (as in "it tastes sweet") *schmecken* <u>shmekken</u>

taxi *das Taxi(s)* <u>tuxee</u>(s); taxi stand *der Taxistand("e)* <u>tuxee-shtunt</u> PL: <u>tuxee-shtenda</u>

tea (drink) *der Tee* <u>tay</u>, OR (afternoon snack of coffee and cake) *Kaffee und Kuchen* <u>kuffay</u> oont <u>kookhen</u>, OR (evening meal) *das Abendessen(-)* <u>ahbent-essen</u>

to teach *unterrichten* <u>oonter-rikhten</u>, OR (as in "it teaches us") *lehren* <u>lairen</u>

teacher (man) *der Lehrer(-)* <u>lairer</u>, OR (woman) *die Lehrerin(nen)* <u>lairerin</u>(en)

team *das Team(s)* <u>teem</u>(s), OR (sport) *die Mannschaft(en)* <u>mun-shufft</u>(en)

to tease *necken* <u>necken</u>, OR (to be joking) *Spaß machen* <u>shpahss</u> mukhen

teenager *der Teenager(-)* <u>teenager</u>, OR *der Teen(s)**, OR *der/die Jugendliche(n)* <u>yoogunt-likha</u>(n)

telephone (See phone)

television *der Fernseher(-)* <u>fairn-zayer</u>; on television *im Fernsehen* im <u>fairn-zayen</u>

to tell (say) *sagen* <u>zahgun</u>, OR (recount) *erzählen* air-<u>tsailen</u>; to tell off *aus'schimpfen* <u>aowss-shimpfen</u>

temperature *die Temperatur(en)* tempera-<u>toor</u>(en); to have a temperature *Fieber haben* <u>feeber</u> hahben

temporary *vorübergehend* for-<u>oohber</u>-gayent

tennis *Tennis* [n] <u>tennis</u>

tent *das Zelt(e)* <u>tselt</u>(a) (See also campsite)

term (school) *das Halbjahr(e)* <u>hulp-yar</u>(a), OR (six-month university term) *das Semester(-)* zay-<u>mester</u>

terrible *schrecklich* <u>shrek-likh</u>

terrific *sagenhaft* <u>zahgun-huft</u>, OR *geil** <u>ghyle</u>

than *als* <u>ults</u>

to thank *danken* [+ dat] <u>dunken</u>

thank you *danke schön* <u>dunka</u> shurn

thanks *danke* <u>dunka</u>

that (as in "that's good") *das* <u>duss</u>; that one *der¹/die¹/das¹ da* <u>dair/dee/duss</u> dah

the *der¹* [m] <u>dair</u>, OR *die¹* [f, pl] <u>dee</u>, OR *das¹* [n] <u>duss</u>

to swim *schwimmen*

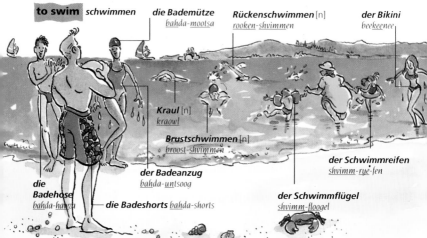

die Bademütze <u>bahda-mootsa</u>

Rückenschwimmen [n] <u>rooken-shvimmen</u>

der Bikini <u>beekeenee</u>

Kraul [n] <u>kraowl</u>

Brustschwimmen [n] <u>broost-shvimmen</u>

der Schwimmreifen <u>shvimm-rye-fen</u>

der Badeanzug <u>bahda-untsoog</u>

der Schwimmflügel <u>shvimm-floogel</u>

die Badehose <u>bahda-hawza</u>

die Badeshorts <u>bahda-shorts</u>

theatre *das Theater(-)* _tay-ahter_
their *ihr* [m, n] _eer_, OR *ihre* [f, pl] _eera_ (*ihr/ihre* change according to gender and case in the same way as *ein/eine*. See Articles p. 44.)
then *dann* _dun_
there *dort* _dort_, OR *da* _dah_, OR (with motion, as in "she went there") *dorthin* dort-_hin_, OR *dahin* dah-_hin_; there is/are *da ist/sind* dah isst/zint, OR *es gibt* [+ acc] ess _ghipt_
these *diese*¹ _deeza_, OR *die*¹ *hier** _dee_ heer
they *sie* _zee_, OR *die** _dee_,
thick *dick* _dik_, OR (stupid) *blöd** _blurd_
thief (man) *der Dieb(e)* _deeb_(a), OR (woman) *die Diebin(nen)* _deebin_(en)
thin *dünn* _doon_, OR (slim) *schlank* _shlunk_
thing *die Sache(n)* _zukha_(n), OR (object) *das Ding(e)* _ding_(a)
things (belongings) *die Sachen* [pl] _zukhan_
to think (believe) *glauben* _glaowben_, OR (consider) *denken* _dengken_, OR (reckon) *meinen* _my-nen_
thirsty: to be thirsty *Durst haben* _doorst hahben_
this *dieser*¹ [m] _deezer_, OR *diese*¹ [f] _deeza_, OR *dieses*¹ [n] _deezess_; this one *der¹/die¹/das¹ hier* _dair/dee/duss_ heer ; this morning/evening *heute morgen/abend* _hoyta morgan/ahbent_
those *die*¹ *da* _dee_ dah
thread *der Faden(¨)* _fahden_ PL: _faiden_
threat *die Bedrohung(en)* _bedrawoong_(en)
to threaten *bedrohen* _bedrawen_
thrill *der Nervenkitzel(-)* _nairven-kitsel_
thriller (film, book) *der Krimi(s)** _krimmee_(s)
throat *die Kehle(n)* _kaila_(n); sore throat *Halsschmerzen* [pl] _hults-shmairtsen_
through *durch* [+ acc] _doorkh_
to throw *werfen* _vairfen_; to throw away/out *weg*ʼ*werfen* _vek-vairfen_; to throw up (be sick) *brechen* _brekhen_
thug *der Schlägertyp(en)* _shlaigertoop_(en)
Thursday *Donnerstag* [m] _donnerstahg_
ticket *die Karte(n)* _karta_(n), OR (travel) *die Fahrkarte(n)* _far-karta_(n), OR (plane) *die Flugkarte(n)* _floog-karta_(n); ticket machine *der Fahrkartenautomat(en)* _farkarten-aowtawmaht_(en); ticket office (theatre) *die Kasse(n)* _kussa_(n), OR (travel) *der Fahrkartenschalter(-)* _farkarten-shullter_
to tickle *kitzeln* _kitseln_
tie *die Krawatte(n)* _kruvutta_(n)
to tie *binden* _binden_; to tie a knot *einen Knoten machen* ine-en k-_nawten_ _mukhen_
tights *die Strumpfhose(n)* _shtroomf-hawza_(n)
time *die Zeit(en)* _tsyte_(-en), OR (occasion) *das*

what time is it? *wieviel Uhr ist es?*

Viertel nach neun _feertel nakh noyn_

drei Uhr _dry_ oor

zehn vor acht _tsain_ for ukht

elf Uhr zwanzig _elf_ oor _tsvuntsikh_

Viertel vor eins _feertel_ for _ine_-ts

halb elf² _hulp_ _elf_

Mittag _mittahg_ Mitternacht _mitternukht_

Mal(e) _mahl_(a); on time *pünktlich* _poonkt_-likh; what time is it? *wieviel Uhr ist es?* _veefeel oor isst es_ (See also picture above)
timetable (transport) *der Fahrplan(¨e)* _farplahn_ PL: _far-plaina_
tip (end) *die Spitze(n)* _shpitsa_(n), OR (money) *das Trinkgeld(er)* _trink-gelt_ PL: _trink-gelder_
tissue (hanky) *das Papiertaschentuch(¨er)* _pupeer-tushen-tookh_ PL: _pupeer-tushen-tooh-kher_
to (towards) *zu* [+ dat] _tsoo_, OR (into, and with [f], [m] or [pl] countries) *in* _in_, OR (with [n] countries) *nach* _nakh_ , OR (as in "ten to four") *vor* _for_
toast *der Toast(e)* _lawst_(a)
today *heute* _hoyta_
together *zusammen* _tsoo-zummen_
toilet *die Toilette(n)* _twuletta_(n); ladies/gents *Damen/Herren* _dahmen/hairen_; toilet paper *das Toilettenpapier* _twuletten-pupeer_
toll *der Zoll(¨e)* _tsol_ PL: _tsurla_
tomato *die Tomate(n)* _lawmahta_(n); tomato sauce *die Tomatensoße* _lawmahten-zawssa_
tomorrow *morgen* _morgan_; tomorrow morning *morgen früh* _morgan-frooh_
tongue *die Zunge(n)* _tsoong-a_(n)
tonight *heute abend* _hoyta-ahbent_

1: This word changes according to gender and case, see Articles, p. 44. **2**: In German you say "half before eleven" rather than "half past ten", e.g. *elf* = eleven, but *halb elf* = half past ten.

too (too much) **zu** _tsoo_, OR (also) **auch** _aowkh_

tool das Werkzeug(e) _vairk-tsoyg(a)_ (See also picture opposite)

tooth der Zahn(¨e) _tsahn_ PL: _tsaina_ (See also ache picture)

toothbrush die Zahnbürste(n) _tsahn-boohrsta(n)_

toothpaste die Zahnpasta _tsahn-pusta_

top (highest part) die Spitze(n) _shpitsa(n)_, OR (lid) der Deckel(-) _deckel_, OR (item of clothing) das Top(s) _top(s)_

torch (pocket) die Taschenlampe(n) _tushen-lumpa(n)_, OR (flaming) die Fackel(n) _fukkel(n)_

train der Zug

die Abfahrtstafel _upfahrts-tahfel_

ARRIVALS ANKUNFT | DEPARTURES ABFAHRT

die Ankunftstafel _unkoonfts-tahfel_   der Fahrkartenschalter _farkarten-shulter_

der Büfettwagen _boofett-vahgun_

Nichtraucher _nikhtraowkher_

der Speisewagen _shpy-za-vahgun_

der Liegewagen _leega-vahgun_   der Bahnhofsvorsteher _bahnhawfs-forshtayer_

der Gepäckwagen _gepek-vahgun_

to touch an'fassen _un-fussen_

tour (trip) die Tour(en) _toor(en)_, OR (music) die Tournee(n) _toor-nay(en)_; package tour die Pauschalreise(n) _paow-shahl-rye-za(n)_

tourist der Tourist(en)[1] _toorist(en)_; tourist office das Fremdenverkehrsamt(¨er) _fremden-fairkairz-umt_ PL: _fremden-fairkairz-emter_

towel das Handtuch(¨er) _hunt-tookh_ PL: _hunt-toohkher_

town die Stadt(¨e) _shtut_ PL: _shtetta_; town centre die Stadtmitte _shtut-mitta_; old town die Altstadt _ult-shtut_; town hall das Rathaus(¨er) _raht-haowss_ PL: _raht-hoyzer_

tracksuit der Trainingsanzug(¨e) _trainings-untsoog_ PL: _trainings-untsoohga_

traffic der Verkehr _fairkair_; traffic jam die Verkehrsstauung(en) _fairkairs-shtaow-oong(en)_; traffic lights die Ampel(n) _umpel(n)_

train der Zug(¨e) _tsoog_ PL: _tsooh-ga_ (See also picture left)

to train (for sport) trainieren _traineeren_

trainers die Trainingsschuhe [pl] _trainings-shoo-a_

tram die Straßenbahn(en) _shtrahssenbahn(en)_; tram stop die Straßenbahnhaltestelle(n) _shtrahssenbahn-hulta-shtella(n)_

tramp der Tramp(s) _tremp(s)_

to translate übersetzen _oohber-zetsen_

to travel reisen _rye-zen_

travel agency das Reisebüro(s) _rye-za-boohraw(s)_

traveller der/die Reisende(n) _rye-zenda(n)_; traveller's cheque der Reisescheck(s) _rye-za-shek(s)_

tree der Baum(¨e) _baowm_ PL: _boyma_

trendy in _in_, OR trendy*, OR cool*

trip (long) die Reise(n) _rye-za(n)_, OR (short) der Ausflug(¨e) _owss-floog_ PL: _owss-floohga_

trolley (for baggage) der Gepäckwagen(-) _gepek-vahgun_, OR (supermarket) der Einkaufswagen(-) _ine-kaowfs-vahgun_

trouble der Kummer _koommer_

trousers die Hose(n) _hawza(n)_

true wahr _var_

to trust vertrauen [+ dat] _fair-traowen_

to try (attempt) versuchen _fair-zookhen_, OR (test) probieren _prawbeeren_

T-shirt das T-shirt(s)

Tuesday Dienstag [m] _deens-tahg_

tuna der Thunfisch(e) _toon-fish(a)_

tunnel der Tunnel(-) _toonnel_

to turn (rotate) drehen _drayen_, OR (to turn left/right in car) ab'biegen _up-beegun_; to turn around/back sich um'drehen _zikh oom-drayen_;

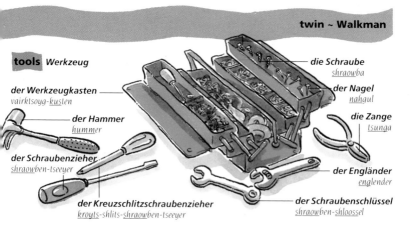

tools *Werkzeug*

die Schraube *shraowba*

der Werkzeugkasten *vairktsoyg-kusten*

der Nagel *nahgul*

der Hammer *hummer*

die Zange *tsunga*

der Schraubenzieher *shraowben-tseeyer*

der Engländer *englender*

der Kreuzschlitzschraubenzieher *krouts-shlits-shraowben-tseeyer*

der Schraubenschlüssel *shraowben-shloossel*

---

to turn down (volume) *leiser stellen* *lye-zer shtellen*; to turn off (light/TV) *aus'machen* *owss-mukhen*; to turn on (light/TV) *an'machen* *un-mukhen*; to turn up (volume) *lauter stellen* *laowter shtellen*, or (arrive) *auf'tauchen* *owf-taowkhen*
twin (brother/sister) *der Zwilling(e)* *tsvilling(a)*
typical *typisch* *toopish*
tyre *der Reifen(-)* *rye-fen*; tyre pressure *der Reifendruck* *rye-fen-drook*

ugly *häßlich* *hesslikh*
umbrella *der Regenschirm(e)* *raigun-sheerm(a)*
under *unter* [+ acc or dat]² *oonter*
underground (trains) *die U-Bahn* *oo-bahn*
to understand *verstehen* *fair-shtayen*
underwear *die Unterwäsche* *oontervesha*
unemployed *arbeitslos* *arbytes-lawss*
unemployment *die Arbeitslosigkeit* *arbytes-lawzikh-kyte*
unfortunately *leider* *lye-der*
United States *die Vereinigten Staaten* [pl] *fair-ine-igten shtahten*
university *die Universität(en)* *oo-nee-vair-zitait(en)*, or *die Uni(s)* *oo-nee(s)*
unusual *ungewöhnlich* *oon-gevurnlikh*, or (exceptional) *außergewöhnlich* *ousser-gevurnlikh*
up: to go/walk up *hinauf'steigen* *hinaowf-shtye-gun*
urgent *dringend* *dring-ent*
us *wir* *veer*, or (in acc. and dat. case) *uns* *oonts* (For more about Cases, see p. 44)
to use *benutzen* *benootsen*
used: to be used to *an* [+acc] *gewöhnt sein* *un (...) gevurnt zyne*
useful *nützlich* *noots-likh*
useless (of no use) *nutzlos* *noots-lawss*; he/she is useless *er/sie ist zu nichts nütze* *air/zee ist tsoo nikhts nootsa*
usual *gewöhnlich* *gevurnlikh*

vacation *die Ferien* [pl] *faireeyen*
vaccination *die Impfung(en)* *imp-foong(en)*
valid *gültig* *gooltikh*
valuables *die Wertsachen* [pl] *vairt-zukhen*
vanilla *Vanille* [f] *vuneelya*
vegetables *das Gemüse* *gamoohza*
vegetarian *vegetarisch* *ve-get-ahrish*
very *sehr* *zair*, or *unheimlich** *oon-hyme-likh*
video *das Video(s)* *vidai-aw(s)*
view (sight) *die Aussicht* *aow-sikht*
village *das Dorf(¨er)* *dorf* PL: *durfer*
vineyard *der Weinberg(e)* *vyne-bairg(a)*
to visit *besuchen* *bezookhen*
vital *unbedingt notwendig* *oonbedinkt nawt-vendikh*
volleyball *Volleyball* [m] *vollay-bul*
to vote *wählen* *vailen*

wacky *verrückt* *fair-rookt*
to waffle *schwafeln* *shvahfeln*
wage *der Lohn(¨e)* *lawn* PL: *lurna*
waist *die Taille(n)* *tie-ya(n)*
waistcoat *die Weste(n)* *vesta(n)*
to wait *warten* *varten*
waiter *der Kellner(-)* *kellner*
waiting room (station) *der Wartesaal* *varta-zahl* PL: *Wartesäle* *varta-zaila*, or (doctor's, dentist's) *das Wartezimmer(-)* *varta-tsimmer*
waitress *die Kellnerin(nen)* *kellnerin(en)*
to wake up (yourself) *auf'wachen* *owf-vukhen*, or (someone else) *auf'wecken* *owf-vekken*
Wales *Wales* [n] *vales*
walk *der Spaziergang(¨e)* *shputseergung* PL: *shputseergng-a*, or (stroll) *der Bummel(-)* *boommel*, or (hike) *die Wanderung(en)* *vunderoong(en)*
to walk *gehen* *gayen*, or *laufen* *laowfen*
Walkman® *der Walkman(s)®* *vawkmun(s)*

1: If you are talking about a female, add *in* (*innen* in the plural). **2**: If your sentence involves movement, use the accusative case; if not, use the dative. For more about cases, see p. 44.

wallet *die Brieftasche(n)* _breef-tusha(n)_

to want *wollen* _vollen_ (See Modal verbs p. 45)

war *der Krieg(e)* _kreeg(a)_

warm *warm* _vahrm_

warning *die Warnung(en)* _vahrnoong(en)_

to wash *waschen* _vushen_, OR (yourself) *sich waschen* zikh _vushen_; to wash up *ab'spülen* _up-shpoohlen_

washing: washing machine *die Waschmaschine(n)* _vush-musheena(n)_; washing powder *das Waschpulver(-)* _vush-poolver_; washing-up liquid *das Spülmittel(-)* _shpoohl-mittel_

wasp *die Wespe(n)* _vesspa(n)_

waste (of time/food/money etc.) *die Verschwendung(en)* _fair-shvendoong(en)_

to waste *verschwenden* _fairshvenden_

watch *die Armbanduhr(en)* _armbunt-oor(en)_, OR *die Uhr(en)* _oor(en)_

to watch (look at) *zu'schauen* _tsoo-shaowen_

water *das Wasser* _vusser_ (See also picture above right)

waterproof *wasserdicht* _vusserdikht_

way (direction) *die Richtung(en)* _rikhtoong(en)_, OR (route) *der Weg(e)* _vaig(a)_, OR (manner) *die Art und Weise* _art oont vye-za_; no way! *auf keinen Fall!* _ouf kye-nen fal_; get out of the way! *weg da*!* _vek dah_; by the way *übrigens* _ooh-brigents_

we *wir* _veer_

to wear *tragen* _trahgen_ (See also Verbs p. 45); to wear out (exhaust) *erschöpfen* _air-shurpfen_, OR (overuse) *ab'nutzen* _up-nootsen_

weather *das Wetter* _vetter_; what's the weather like? *wie ist das Wetter?* _vee isst duss vetter_; weather forecast *die Wettervorhersage(n)* _vetter-forhair-zahga(n)_ (See also picture below)

Wednesday *Mittwoch* [m] _mitvokh_

week *die Woche(n)* _vokha(n)_

weekend *das Wochenende(n)* _vokhen-enda(n)_

weight *das Gewicht(e)* _gevikht(a)_; to lose weight *ab'nehmen* _up-naimen_; to put on weight *zu'nehmen* _tsoo-naimen_

water *Wasser* der Eiswürfel _ite-voohrfel_
das Mineralwasser ohne Kohlensäure _minairahl-vusser awna kawlenzoyra_
der Wasserfall _vusserful_
das Mineralwasser mit Kohlensäure _minairahl-vusser mit kawlenzoyra_
ein Glas Wasser _ine glahss vusser_

weird (strange) *seltsam* _zeltzahm_, OR (creepy) *unheimlich* _oon-hyme-likh_

welcome *willkommen* _villkommen_; you're welcome! *bitte sehr!* _bitta zair_

well *gut* _goot_; well-cooked *durch(gebraten)* _doorkh(gebrahten)_; well-known *bekannt* _bekunt_; to feel well *sich wohl fühlen* zikh _vawl foohlen_

Welsh *walisisch* _vuleezish_, OR (man) *Waliser(-)* _vuleezer_, OR (woman) *Waliserin(nen)* _vuleezerin(en)_

west *der Westen* _vesten_

wet *naß* _nuss_

what *was* _vuss_; what for? *wozu?* _vawtsoo_; what about? *worüber?* _vawroohber_

wheel *das Rad("er)* _raht_ PL: _raider_; steering wheel *das Lenkrad("er)* _lenkraht_ PL: _lenkraider_

wheelchair *der Rollstuhl("e)* _rol-shtool_ PL: _rol-shtooh-la_

when (at what time) *wann* _vun_, OR (if, whenever) *wenn* _ven_

where *wo* _vaw_; where from? *woher?* _vawhair_; where to? *wohin?* _vawhin_

which *welcher* [m] _velkher_, OR *welche* [f, pl] _velkha_, OR *welches* [n] _velkhess_ (These words change according to gender and case in the same way as *der*, *die* and *das*, see p. 44)

es regnet ess _raignet_   *es ist bedeckt* ess isst _bedekt_   *es ist sonnig* ess isst _zonnikh_   *es schneit* ess _shnyte_

wine *der Wein* : *der Weinberg* vine-bairg
der Rotwein rawt-vine
— *der Weißwein* vice-vine
der Rosé raw-zay

der Korkenzieher *der Korken*
korken-tseeyer korken

ein Glas Wein ine glahss vine

while (at same time) *während* vairent
white *weiß* vice
who *wer* vair, OR (in acc. case) *wen* vain, OR (in dat. case) *wem* vaim
whole *ganz* gunts
why *warum* vahroomm
wide *breit* bryte
wild (not tame) *wild* vilt, OR (angry) *wütend* voohtent
to win *gewinnen* gavinnen
wind *der Wind(e)* vint PL: vinda (See also picture below)
window *das Fenster(-)* fenster
windscreen *die Windschutzscheibe(n)* vintshoots-shy-ba(n)
windsurfer (board) *das Surfbrett(er)* zoorf-brett(er)
wine *der Wein(e)* vyne(-a) (See also picture above)
winter *der Winter(-)* vinter
wish *der Wunsch("e)* voonsh(a); best wishes *herzliche Grüße* hairtslikha groohssa
to wish (hope for) *wünschen* voontschen
with *mit* [+ dat] mit
without *ohne* [+ acc] awna
woman *die Frau(en)* fraow(en), OR (lady) *die Dame(n)* dahma(n)
wonderful *wunderbar* voonderbar

wood (material) *das Holz("er)* hollts PL: hurltser, OR (forest) *der Wald("er)* vult PL: velder
wool *die Wolle(n)* volla(n)
word *das Wort("er)* vort PL: vurter; word processing *die Textverarbeitung* textfair-ar-bye-toong
work *die Arbeit(en)* ar-byte(-en)
to work *arbeiten* ar-byte-en, OR *schuften** shooften, OR (function) *funktionieren* foonktsee-aw-neeren, OR (go well) *klappen** kluppen
world *die Welt(en)* velt(en)
worried *besorgt* bezorkt
worry *die Sorge(n)* zorga(n); not to worry! *keine Sorge!* kye-na zorga
worse *schlimmer* shlimmer
to write *schreiben* shrye-ben
writer (man) *der Schriftsteller(-)* shrift-shteller, OR (woman) *die Schriftstellerin(nen)* shrift-shtellerin(en)
wrong (incorrect) *falsch* fulsh, OR (unfair) *ungerecht* oon-gerekht; to be wrong (not right) *unrecht haben* oon-rekht hahben, OR (mistaken) *sich täuschen* zikh toyshen; what's wrong? *was ist los?* vuss isst lawss

year *das Jahr(e)* yar(a)
yellow *gelb* gelp
yes *ja* yah, OR (after negative) *doch* dokh
yesterday *gestern* guess-tern
yet: not yet *noch nicht* nokh nikht
yogurt *der Joghurt(-)* yogoort
you (casual) *du* doo, OR (casual [pl]) *ihr* eer, OR (polite) *Sie* zee, OR (in acc. case) *dich* dikh, OR *euch* oykh, OR *Sie* zee, OR (in dat. case) *dir* deer, OR *euch* oykh, OR *Ihnen* eenen (See also p. 44)
you (as in "you can never tell") *man* mun
young *jung* yoong
your (casual) *dein* [m, n] dine, OR *deine* [f, pl] dine-a, OR (casual plural) *euer* [m, n] oyer, OR *eure* [f, pl] oyra, OR (polite) *Ihr* [m, n] eer, OR *Ihre* [f, pl] eera (These words change in the same way as *ein/eine*, see p. 44)
youth hostel *die Jugendherberge(n)* yoogunt-hairbairga(n)
zip *der Reißverschluß* PL: *Reißverschlüsse* rice-fairshlooss(a)

es gibt ein Gewitter
ess gipt ine gevitter

es ist kalt
ess isst kult

es ist sehr warm
es isst zair vahrm

es ist windig ess isst vindikh

Getting by in German

You don't have to make a perfect sentence to be understood, but knowing a little about the way German works will help. These notes provide some basic tips about the language.

Nouns (names of things, e.g. "guitar")

All German nouns are written with a capital letter. They are either masculine [m], feminine [f] or neuter [n]. This is called their gender. The word for "the" is **der** for [m] words; **die** for [f] words and **das** for [n]. The words for "a", "an" and "one" are **ein** for [m] and [n] words, and **eine** for [f] words.

German has lots of long words. Often these are made up of two or more shorter ones joined together, e.g. **die Bushaltestelle** (bus stop) is **Bus** (bus) + **halte** (stopping) + **Stelle** (place).

Plurals (more than one, e.g. "guitars")

The plural word for "the" is **die**. Most nouns are made plural by adding one or two letters and/or an umlaut (¨) over the last "a", "o", or "u" (or over the "a" of "au"). This dictionary shows you in brackets which letters to add in the plural.

Cases (special forms of German words)

German nouns (and pronouns[1]) go into different "cases" depending on the job they do in a sentence. It is useful to know about this because words like "the", which are used with the noun, change a little according to the case.

The **nominative** case is used for the person or thing doing the action. In **der Mann ißt den Kuchen** (the man is eating the cake), **der Mann** (the man) is nominative. Words listed in the dictionary are listed in this case.

The **accusative** case is used for the direct object (the person or thing the action has a direct effect on). In the previous example **den Kuchen** (the cake) is accusative.

The **dative** case is used for the indirect object (the person or thing the action has

an indirect effect on). For example, in **der Junge gibt dem Mann den Kuchen** (the boy gives the man the cake), **dem Mann** (the man) is dative.

Articles (der, die, das and ein, eine)

Sometimes the words for "the" (**der, die, das**) and "a" (**ein, eine**) change, depending on the case of the noun you are using them with. This chart shows you how:

	[m]	[f]	[n]	[pl]
Nom:	der	die	das	die
Acc:	den	die	das	die
Dat:	dem	der	dem	den
Nom:	ein	eine	ein	-
Acc:	einen	eine	ein	-
Dat:	einem	einer	einem	-

Dieser, diese, dieses (this) follow the same pattern as **der, die, das**.

Prepositions (words like "of", "to", etc.)

Some German prepositions are always followed by words in the accusative; others are always followed by the dative. In the English-German list (p. 4-43), each preposition is listed with the case that follows it.

A few prepositions can be followed by either the accusative or the dative, depending on the sentence. If the sentence involves movement, e.g. she's going into the library, use the accusative: **sie geht in die Bibliothek**; if not, e.g. she is in the library, use the dative: **sie ist in der Bibliothek**.

Dem and das with prepositions

When **dem** (dat. of "the") or **das** (acc. of "the") come after a preposition, the two words often join to form one, e.g. **zu** + **dem** = **zum** (to the); **in** + **das** = **ins** (in the).

Using du, ihr and Sie

German has three words for "you": **du**, **ihr** and **Sie** (and for related words, e.g. **dein**, **euer** and **Ihr** all mean "your"). **Du** is singular and informal; use it with a friend or a child. **Ihr** is plural and informal. When

---

1: A pronoun is a word that replaces a noun, e.g. in "Have you seen my friend? She's wearing a yellow jacket", "friend" is a noun, "she" is a pronoun.

talking to one or more strangers or older people, use the polite word for "you", **Sie**.

Verbs *(action words, e.g. "to run")*

Most German verbs end in **en** in the infinitive (the basic form, e.g. **machen** = to do, to make), and many follow a pattern. To talk about the present, drop **en** and add one of the endings underlined below[2]:

I make	*ich mach<u>e</u>*
you make	*du mach<u>st</u>*
he/she/it makes	*er/sie/es mach<u>t</u>*
we make	*wir mach<u>en</u>*
you make	*ihr mach<u>t</u>*
they make	*sie mach<u>en</u>*
you make (polite)	*Sie mach<u>en</u>*

Many verbs also have an extra change in the **du** and **er/sie/es** forms. Here are these forms for some common verbs:

	du	*er/sie/es*
geben (to give)	*gibst*	*gibt*
sehen (to see)	*siehst*	*sieht*
essen (to eat)	*ißt*	*ißt*
fahren (to go)	*fährst*	*fährt*
haben (to have)	*hast*	*hat*
tragen (to wear)	*trägst*	*trägt*
nehmen (to take)	*nimmst*	*nimmt*
werden (to become)	*wirst*	*wird*

Some verbs, such as **sein** (to be), **tun** (to do/to put*), or **wissen** (to know), change in most forms:

	sein	*tun*	*wissen*
ich	*bin*	*tue*	*weiß*
du	*bist*	*tust*	*weißt*
er/sie/es	*ist*	*tut*	*weiß*
wir/sie/Sie	*sind*	*tun*	*wissen*
ihr	*seid*	*tut*	*wißt*

Separable verbs

Many German verbs are made up of two parts, e.g. **ankommen** (to arrive) = **an** (at) + **kommen** (to come). The first part goes to the end of the sentence, e.g. **sie kommt morgen an** (she is arriving tomorrow).

Modal verbs

There are six "modal" verbs: **können** (to be able to, can), **müssen** (to have to,

must), **wollen** (to want to), **dürfen** (to be allowed to, may), **sollen** (to be supposed to, should), **mögen** (to like to). These are often used with other verbs, which must go to the end of the sentence, e.g. **ich will Tennis spielen** (I want to play tennis).

Reflexive verbs *(verbs with "sich")*

Some German verbs, called reflexive verbs, begin with **sich** in the infinitive. They usually mean an action you do to yourself, e.g. **sich sonnen** = to sunbathe. With **ich** use **mich**; with **du** use **dich**; with **er**, **sie**, **es** and **Sie** use **sich**; with **wir** use **uns** and with **ihr** use **euch**. E.g. **ich sonne mich**, **du sonnst dich** etc.

Questions

To make a question, put the subject (the person doing the action) after the verb, e.g. **sie weiß** = she knows; **weiß sie?** = does she know?

Negatives

To make a sentence negative, add **nicht**. For example, **ich will** = I want to; **ich will nicht** = I don't want to.

To say "not a" or "no" use **kein**, e.g. **es gibt keinen Bus** (there's no bus). The word **kein** changes in the same way as **ein**. In the plural use **keine** (nom. and acc.) and **keinen** (dat.).

Pronunciation

The best way to pronounce German well is to copy a German speaker. The pronunciation hints in the English-German list (p. 4-43) will help you. Here are a few extra tips:

- "**ch**" (shown as *kh* in the hints) is usually like the "ch" in the Scottish word "loch". Sometimes it is closer to "sh".

- "**g**" (shown as *g*, *gh* or *gu*) is usually said as in the English word "get", but on the end of a word it is often like the German **ch**.

- "**u**" and "**ü**" (shown as *oo* or *ooh*) can sound like "oo" in "foot", "oo" in "food", or a bit like the "u" in music but without the "yuh" sound.

2: You can use these forms to talk about what you do, what you are doing and what you will do, e.g. **ich mache** can mean "I make", "I am making" or "I will make".

ab from
ab'biegen to turn
der Abend(e) evening; *zu Abend essen* to have dinner
das Abendessen(-) supper
das Abenteuer(-) adventure
aber but, OR however
abergläubisch superstitious
ab'fahren to leave
die Abfahrt(en) departure
die Abfahrtstafel(n) departure board
der Abfall("e) rubbish, OR litter, OR waste
die Abfallbeseitigung rubbish/garbage disposal
der Abfalleimer(-) bin
die Abfertigung (airport) check-in
sich ab'finden mit to put up with
ab'fliegen (plane) to take off
der Abflug("e) departure
die Abflughalle(n) departure lounge
abgeschaltet (switched) off
ab'hauen* to clear off, OR to split (leave); *hau ab!** get lost!
das Abitur German exams taken at end of secondary/high school
die Abkürzung(en) short cut, OR abbreviation
ab'laufen to run out (expire)
ab'lehnen to refuse
ab'lenken to distract
ab'nehmen to lose weight
ab'nutzen to wear out (overuse)
ab'raten to put off, OR to warn
ab'sagen to cancel
ab'schließen to lock
ab'setzen to take off (hat), OR to drop off (a person)
absichtlich on purpose
ab'spülen to wash up
die Abspüllösung(en) (contact lens) rinsing solution
adoptiert adopted
die Adresse(n) address
ähnlich (wie) similar (to)
aktuell up to date
der Akzent(e) accent
akzeptieren to accept
albern silly
das Album (PL: *Alben*) album
der Alkohol alcohol
alkoholfrei non-alcoholic
alkoholisch alcoholic
alle all, OR everybody

allein alone, OR by yourself
die Allergie(n) allergy
alles all of it, OR everything
allgemein general
der Alltag everyday life
der Alptraum("e) nightmare
als when, OR than
also so, OR therefore, OR right
alt old; *wie alt ...?* how old ...?
das Alter(-) age
der Altglascontainer(-) bottle bank
altmodisch old-fashioned
die Altstadt old town
Amerika [n] America
Amerikaner(-)[1] American (man)
amerikanisch American
die Ampel(n) traffic lights
das Amtszeichen dialling tone
sich amüsieren to have fun
an on, OR at
die Ananas(-) pineapple
an'bieten to offer
andere (OR *anderer* OR *anderes*) other
ändern to change
anders als different from/to
anderswo somewhere else
die Änderung(en) change
an'ekeln to put off (disgust)
der Anfall("e) fit; *der epileptische Anfall* epileptic fit
der Anfang("e) start, OR beginning
der Anfänger(-)[1] beginner
an'fassen to touch
an'geben to show off, OR to boast, OR (sport) to serve
angeln to fish
an'greifen to attack
die Angst("e) fear; *Angst haben* to be scared
an'halten to stop
der Anhänger(-)[1] supporter, OR (car) trailer, OR (jewellery) pendant
der Anker(-) anchor
an'kommen to arrive; *es kommt darauf an* it depends
die Ankunftstafel(n) arrival board
an'machen to switch on, OR (slang) to chat up
die Anmeldung(en) registration
an'nehmen to accept, OR to suppose
die Annonce(n) advertisement

an'quatschen* to chat up
der Anruf(e) phone call
der Anrufbeantworter(-) answering machine
an'rufen to phone
der Anschluß connection
die Ansichtskarte(n) picture postcard
ansteckend contagious, OR infectious
der Anstecker(-) badge
die Antibabypille(n) contraceptive pill
das Antibiotikum (PL: *Antibiotika*) antibiotic
antiseptisch antiseptic
die Antwort(en) answer
antworten to reply
die Anzahlung(en) deposit
die Anzeige(n) advertisement, OR (police) report, OR (computer) display
sich an'ziehen to get dressed
der Anzug("e) suit
der Apfel(") apple
der Apfelkuchen(-) apple cake, OR apple tart
die Apfelsine(n) orange
der Apfelstrudel(-) apple strudel (apple in puff pastry)
der Apfelwein cider
die Apotheke(n) pharmacy
die Aprikose(n) apricot
April [m] April
die Arbeit(en) job, OR work
arbeiten to work
arbeitslos unemployed
die Arbeitslosigkeit unemployment
ärgerlich annoying
ärgern to annoy; *sich ärgern* to be/get annoyed
arm poor
der Arm(e) arm
das Armband("er) bracelet
die Armbanduhr(en) watch
der Ärmel(-) sleeve
der Ärmelkanal the Channel
der Armreifen(-) bangle
die Art(en) sort, OR way, OR manner
der Artikel(-) article
der Arzt("e)[2] doctor
der Aschenbecher(-) ashtray
Asien [n] Asia
der Asylant(en)[1] asylum seeker
der Atem breath
der Atemregler(-) regulator
atmen to breathe

1: For a female the word has *in* on the end (*innen* in the plural). **2**: For a female the word is *die Ärztin(nen)*.

attraktiv attractive
auch also, OR too
auf on, OR up, OR open; *auf ... zu* towards
die Aufführung(en) (theatre) performance
aufgeregt excited, OR nervous
aufgeweckt bright (clever)
auf'hängen to hang (up)
auf'heben to keep, OR to pick up (lift)
auf'hetzen to stir (up)
auf'hören to stop
der Aufkleber(-) sticker, OR badge
auf'legen to hang up (phone)
auf'machen to open
die Aufnahme(n) photo, OR recording
auf'nehmen to record
auf'passen to pay attention; *auf'passen auf* to watch, OR to keep an eye on, OR to look after
sich auf'regen to get excited
aufregend exciting
auf'stehen to get up
auf'tauchen to turn up (arrive)
auf'teilen to split (share out)
auf'wachen to wake up
auf'wärmen to warm up
auf'wecken to wake (someone) up
auf Wiederhören goodbye (on the phone)
auf Wiedersehen goodbye
der Aufzug("e) lift
das Auge(n) eye
der Augenblick(e) moment; *Augenblick mal!* just a moment!
August [m] August
aus from, OR of; *von mir/sich aus* I don't/he doesn't mind
aus'bilden to train, OR to educate
die Ausbildung education (studies), OR training
die Ausfahrt(en) motorway exit
aus'flippen* to freak out
der Ausflug("e) trip
der Ausgang("e) result, OR exit, OR (airport) departure gate
aus'geben to spend (money)
ausgebucht booked up
ausgeschaltet (switched) off
ausgezeichnet excellent
die Auskunft("e) information, OR inquiries
das Ausland: *im/ins Ausland* abroad

der Ausländer(-)[1] foreigner
aus'machen to switch off, OR to arrange, OR to fix
aus'nutzen to take advantage of
aus'richten to tell; *etwas aus'richten* to take a message
sich aus'ruhen to rest
die Ausrüstung(en) equipment
aus'schimpfen to tell off
der Ausschlag("e) rash
aus'sehen to look (as in "to look good/ill")
außer except
außergewöhnlich unusual
die Aussicht view
der Austausch exchange (holiday)
aus'stehen to stand (endure), E.G. *ich kann ... nicht ausstehen* I can't stand...
aus'steigen aus to get off (bus, train), OR to drop out of (college/a competition)
die Ausstellung(en) exhibition
Australien [n] Australia
Australier(-)[1] Australian (man)
australisch Australian
der Ausverkauf("e) sale
aus'wählen to pick (choose)
der Ausweis(e) pass, OR identity card
aus'ziehen to take off (clothes), OR to move out
das Auto(s) car
die Autobahn(en) motorway
der Autor(en)[1] author
die Avocado(s) avocado

die Bäckerei(en) baker's
der Backofen("") oven
das Bad("er) bath
der Badeanzug("e) swimming costume
die Badehose(n) swimming trunks
der Bademeister(-) lifeguard
die Bademütze(n) swimming cap
die Badeshorts [pl] bermuda swimming trunks
das Badetuch("er) bath towel
das Badezimmer(-) bathroom
die Bahn railway
der Bahnhof("e) train station
der Bahnhofsvorsteher(-) station master

bald soon
der Balkon(e) balcony
der Ball("e) ball
das Ballett ballet
die Banane(n) banana
die Band(s) band
die Bank(en) bank
die Bank("e) bench
die Bar(s) bar
das Bargeld cash (money)
der Bart("e) beard
die Batterie(n) battery
der Bauch("e) stomach
Bauchschmerzen [pl] stomachache
der Baum("e) tree, OR (sailing) boom
die Baumwolle cotton
der Bazillus (PL: *Bazillen*) bug (germ)
beabsichtigen to intend
beantworten to answer
bedecken to cover
bedeckt (weather) overcast
bedeuten to mean
bedienen to serve; *sich bedienen* to help yourself
die Bedienung service
bedrohen to threaten
die Bedrohung(en) threat
sich beeilen to hurry
der Befehl(e) order, OR (computer) command
behalten to keep
behindert disabled
bei at, E.G. *bei Anna* at Anna's, OR near, E.G. *bei Bonn* near Bonn
beide both
das Bein(e) leg
das Beispiel(e) example
beißen to bite
bekannt famous, OR well-known
der/die Bekannte(n) friend
sich beklagen to complain
bekommen to get (obtain)
beleidigt offended
die Beleidigung(en) insult
beliebt popular
benutzen to use
das Benzin (UK) petrol, OR (US) gas(oline)
bequem comfortable
der Berg(e) mountain
das Bergsteigen mountain climbing
berühmt famous
sich besaufen* to get drunk
beschädigen to damage
beschäftigt busy
beschimpfen to swear at

beschließen to decide
beschreiben to describe
besessen obsessed
die Besichtigungstour(en) sightseeing tour
der Besitzer(-)[1] owner
besoffen* drunk
besorgt worried
besser better
beste (OR *bester* OR *bestes*) best
bestehen to pass (an exam); *auf (...) bestehen* to insist on (something); *bestehen aus* to consist of
bestellen to order
die Bestellung(en) order
der Besuch(e) visit, OR visitor(s)
besuchen to visit
sich betrinken to get drunk
betrunken drunk
das Bett(en) bed
das Bettlaken(-) sheet
der Bettler(-)[1] beggar
die Beule(n) bump
bevor before
bewegen to move
der Beweis(e) proof
bezahlen to pay
der BH(-) bra
die Bibliothek(en) library
das Bier(e) beer; *das helle Bier* lager
der Bikini(s) bikini
das Bild(er) picture
die Bildhauerei sculpture
der Bildschirm(e) screen
billig cheap
binden to tie; *sich binden* to commit yourself
die Bindung(en) binding
der Bioladen(¨) health food shop
biologisch abbaubar biodegradable
die Birne(n) pear
bis bald see you soon
bißchen: *ein bißchen* a bit, OR a little
bitte please, OR you're welcome; *wie bitte?* pardon?
bitter bitter (taste)
die Blase(n) blister, OR bladder, OR bubble
das Blatt(¨er) leaf, OR sheet (of paper)
blau blue, OR (slang) drunk
bleiben to stay (remain)
bleifrei lead-free
der Bleigürtel(-) weight belt

der Bleistift(e) pencil
blind blind
der Blitz(e) lightning, OR (camera) flash
blöd* stupid
blond blond
der Blouson(s) jacket (bomber-style)
die Blume(n) flower
das Blut blood
der Blutdruck blood pressure
bluten to bleed
blutig bloody, OR (steak) rare
Bock: *einen Bock schießen*** to put your foot in it; *keinen Bock haben*** not to feel like (doing something)
der Boden ground
die Bohne(n) bean
die Boje(n) buoy
das Boot(e) boat
der Boß* (PL: *Bosse*) boss
böse angry, OR bad , OR evil
die Botschaft(en) embassy
das Bowling bowling
die Box(en)* speaker (hi-fi)
Brat~ fried E.G. *Bratwurst* fried sausage
der Brauch(¨e) custom
brauchen to need
braun brown
brechen to break, OR to throw up (be sick)
breit wide
die Bremse(n) brake
brennen to burn
der Brief(e) letter
der Brieffreund(e)[1] pen pal
der Briefkasten(¨) post-box
die Briefmarke(n) stamp
die Brieftasche(n) wallet
die Brille(n) glasses
bringen to bring, OR to take
die Brosche(n) brooch
das Brot bread, OR loaf
das Brötchen(-) (bread) roll
die Brücke(n) bridge
der Bruder(¨) brother
brüllen to shout
der Brunnen(-) fountain
die Brust(¨e) breast, OR chest
Brustschwimmen [n] breast-stroke
das Buch(¨er) book
buchen to book
die Buchhandlung(en) bookshop
der Buchstabe(n) letter (of alphabet)
der Buckel(-) bump, OR hump

der Büfettwagen(-) buffet car
das Bügeleisen(-) iron (for clothes)
der Bummel(-) walk, OR stroll
bunt colourful
die Burg(en) castle
der Bürgersteig(e) pavement
das Büro(s) office
die Bürste(n) brush
der Bus(se) bus
der Busbahnhof(¨e) bus station
der Busen(-) bosom
die Bushaltestelle(n) bus stop
die Butter butter

das Café(s) café
der Campingplatz(¨e) campsite
die Cashewnuß (PL: *Cashewnüsse*) cashew nut
das Cello(s) cello
der Champignon(s) mushroom
die Chance(n) chance
das Chaos chaos
der Charakter(e) personality
checken* to check
Cheerleader cheerleader
der Chef(s)[1] boss
Chips (UK) crisps, (US) potato chips
der Chor(¨e) choir
christlich Christian
der Code(s) code
der Comic(s) comic book
cool* cool, OR laid-back, OR trendy, OR casual
der Cousin(s)[2] cousin
die Creme(s) cream

da there; *da ist/sind* there is/ are; *der/die/das da* that one
das Dach(¨er) roof
der Dachgepäckträger(-) roof rack
daheim at home
dahin there
dahinter kommen* to get the low-down
die Dame(n) lady
Damen ladies
die Damenbinde(n) sanitary towel
Dänemark [n] Denmark
dankbar grateful
danke thanks; *danke schön* thank you

danken to thank
dann then
das the, OR it, OR that
das Date(s)* date (meeting with boy/girlfriend)
das Datum (PL: *Daten*) date
die Daunenjacke(n) quilted jacket
DB (*Deutsche Bundesbahn*) [f] German railways
das Deck(s) deck
die Decke(n) blanket
der Deckel(-) top, OR lid
dein (OR *deine*) **your** (casual)
die Demokratie democracy
die Demonstration(en) demonstration
denken to think (consider)
das Denkmal(¨er) monument
denn because
der Deodorant(s) deodorant
deprimierend depressing
der the, OR (slang) it, OR he, OR her, OR him
deutsch German; *auf deutsch* in German
Deutsche(n) German (man or woman)
Deutschland [n] Germany
Dezember [m] December
das Dia(s) (photographic) slide
der Dialekt(e) dialect
die Diät(en) diet
dich you
dick fat, OR thick
die the, OR (slang) her, OR she, OR them, OR they, OR it; *die da* those
der Dieb(e)¹ thief
Dienstag [m] Tuesday
diese (OR *dieser* OR *dieses*) this, OR these
der Diesel diesel
das Ding(e) thing
direkt direct, OR straight
die Diskette(n) floppy disk
die Diskriminierung discrimination
diskutieren to discuss
doch yes
der Dom(e) cathedral
Donnerstag [m] Thursday
doof* stupid
Doppel~ double, E.G. *das Doppelbett* double bed
das Dorf(¨er) village
dort there
die Dose(n) can
der Dosenöffner(-) can opener
der Drachen(-) kite

Drachenfliegen [n] hang-gliding
dran: *du bist dran* it's your go
draußen outside
das Dreckloch(¨er)* dump
drehen to turn, OR (film) to shoot
drin* inside
dringend urgent
drinnen indoors
die Droge(n) drug
der/die Drogensüchtige(n) drug addict
die Drogerie(n) chemist's
drüben over there, OR on the other side
drücken to press
der Drucker(-) printer
der Druckmesser(-) pressure gauge
du you (See also p. 44)
der Duft(¨e) smell (good)
duften to smell (good)
dumm stupid
Dummkopf(¨e)* idiot
die Düne(n) dune
dunkel dark
dünn thin, OR (drink) weak
durch through, OR (caused) by
durch'drehen* to crack, OR to freak out
durcheinander mixed up
das Durcheinander chaos, OR mess
durcheinander'bringen to mix up, OR to confuse
Durchfall [m] (UK) diarrhoea, (US) diarrhea
durch'fallen to fail (exam)
durchgebraten well-cooked
durchschnittlich average
Durst: *Durst haben* to be thirsty
die Dusche(n) shower
sich duschen to have a shower

echt real
die Ecke(n) corner
egal: *es ist mir egal* I don't mind/care; *ist doch egal!* never mind!; *egal wo* anywhere
egoistisch selfish
ehrlich honest
das Ei(er) egg; *das hartgekochte Ei* hard-boiled egg; *das verlorene Ei* poached egg; *das weichgekochte Ei* soft-boiled egg
der Eierbecher(-) eggcup
eifersüchtig jealous

das Eigelb(-) egg yolk
eigenartig odd (strange)
eilig urgent; *es eilig haben* to be in a hurry
ein (OR *eine*) a, an
die Einbahnstraße(n) one way street
sich ein'bilden to imagine
einfach simple, OR single
der Eingang(¨e) entrance
eingebildet stuck-up
einige some, OR a few
einkaufen gehen to go shopping
der Einkaufswagen(-) (supermarket) trolley
ein'laden to invite, OR to ask out
die Einladung(en) invitation
ein'packen to pack
einsam lonely
ein'schließen to lock up, OR to include
das Einschreiben(-) recorded delivery letter
ein'steigen in to get onto
der Eintritt entry, OR admission
einverstanden sein to agree
der Einwanderer(-)¹ immigrant
Einzel~ single E.G. *das Einzelzimmer* single room
das Eis ice, OR ice cream
die Eisbahn(en) ice rink
die Eisdiele(n) ice cream parlour
die Eisenbahn(en) railway
eis'laufen skating (on ice)
der Eiswürfel(-) ice cube
das Eiweiß egg white
ekelhaft disgusting
elektrisch electric
der Ellenbogen(-) elbow
die Eltern [pl] parents
der Empfang(¨e) reception
die Empfängnisverhütung contraception
empfehlen to recommend
empfindlich sensitive
das Ende(n) end
endlich at last
eng narrow, OR (clothes) tight, OR (friends) close
engbefreundet close friends
England [n] England
Engländer(-)¹ English (man)
der Engländer(-) adjustable spanner

englisch English
entdecken to discover
die Entfernung(en) distance
entkommen to get away
die Entschuldigung(en) excuse, OR apology; *Entschuldigung!* excuse me!, OR sorry!
sich entspannen to relax
entspannt relaxed
enttäuscht disappointed
die Entzündung(en) infection
epileptisch epileptic
er he, OR him, OR it
die Erbse(n) pea
die Erdbeere(n) strawberry
das Erdgeschoß ground floor
die Erdnuß (PL: *Erdnüsse*) peanut
die Erfahrung(en) experience
erfinden to invent
der Erfolg(e) hit, OR success; *Erfolg haben* to succeed
erforschen to explore
das Ergebnis(se) result
erinnern to remind; *sich erinnern an* to remember
erkältet sein to have a cold
die Erkältung cold (illness)
erkennen to recognize
erklären to explain
sich erkundigen to find out, OR to get information
die Erlaubnis(se) permission, OR permit
erledigt finished, OR (slang) shattered
erleichtert relieved
ernst serious
erotisch erotic
das Ersatzteil(e) spare part
erschöpfen to wear out
erschöpft exhausted
erschreckt startled, OR frightened
erst not until, OR only
erstaunlich amazing
erste(n) first; *Erste Hilfe* [f] first aid; *das Erste-Hilfe-Set* first aid kit
der/die Erwachsene(n) adult
erzählen to tell

die Erziehung education, OR upbringing
erzielen to score
es it
das Essen food, OR meal
essen to eat
der Essig vinegar
das Eßzimmer(-) dining room
etwas something, OR anything, OR a little; *etwas anderes* something else
Europa [n] Europe
Europäer(-)[1] European (man)
europäisch European
der Euroscheck(s) Eurocheque
evangelisch Protestant
exotisch exotic
extra extra
exzellent excellent

fabelhaft fabulous
das Fach(¨er) (school) subject
der Faden(¨) thread
die Fähre(n) ferry
fahren to drive, OR to ride (bike), OR to go (by car/train)
der Fahrer(-)[1] driver
die Fahrkarte(n) ticket
der Fahrkartenschalter(-) ticket office
der Fahrplan(¨e) timetable
der Fahrpreis(e) fare
das Fahrrad(¨er) bike
der Fahrschein(e) ticket
der Fahrstuhl(¨e) lift, OR elevator
die Fahrt(en) journey, OR trip
fair fair (just)
der Fall(¨e) fall, OR case; *auf keinen Fall!* no way!; *für alle Fälle* just in case
das Fall(en) (sailing) sheet
fallen to fall; *fallen lassen* to drop
der Fallschirm(e) parachute
falsch wrong (incorrect)
die Familie(n) family
der Fan(s) fan, OR supporter
fangen to catch
die Farbe(n) colour
Fasching [m] Shrovetide carnival
das Faßbier(e) beer (on tap)
fast nearly
faul lazy
Februar [m] February
Federball [m] badminton
der Fehler(-) mistake

feiern to celebrate, OR to party
der Feiertag(e) holiday (bank holiday)
der Feigling(e) coward; *Feigling!* I dare you!
feilschen to haggle
das Feinkostgeschäft(e) delicatessen
der Felsbrocken(-) rock, OR boulder
der Felsen(-) cliff, OR rock-face
der Feminist(en)[1] feminist
der Fender(-) fender
das Fenster(-) window
die Ferien [pl] (UK) holidays, (US) vacation
die Fernbedienung(en) remote control
die Ferne distance
das Ferngespräch(e) long-distance phone call
das Fernglas(¨er) binoculars
der Fernseher(-) television
das Fernsprechbuch(¨er) telephone directory
fertig ready, OR finished, OR (slang) exhausted
fertig machen to finish
das Fest(e) festival, OR (slang) party
die Fete(n)* party
das Fett fat
das Feuer(-) fire
die Feuerwehr fire brigade
das Feuerwerk fireworks
das Feuerzeug(e) lighter
das Fieber(-) fever; *Fieber haben* to have a temperature
fies* gross (horrid), OR lousy, OR nasty
der Film(e) (UK) film, OR (US) movie
finden to find, OR to think
der Finger(-) finger; *Finger weg!* hands off!
der Fisch(e) fish, OR (star sign) Pisces
fischen to fish
fit fit
flach flat
die Flasche(n) bottle
der Flaschenöffner(-) bottle opener
der Fleck(en) mark, OR spot; *der blaue Fleck* bruise
das Fleisch meat
die Fleischerei(en) butcher's
die Fliege(n) fly
fliegen to fly
fließend fluent

1: For a female the word has *in* on the end (*innen* in the plural).

Flipper [m] pinball
flirten to flirt
der Flohmarkt("e) flea market
das Floß("e) raft
die Flosse(n) (diving) flipper
fluchen to swear
der Flug("e) flight
der Flügel(-) wing, OR grand piano
die Fluggesellschaft(en) airline
der Flughafen(") airport
die Flugkarte(n) plane ticket
der Flugsteig(e) airport gate
das Flugzeug(e) plane
der Fluß (PL: *Flüsse*) river
folgen to follow, OR to obey
der Fön(e) hair-dryer
Football: *American Football* [m] American football
die Form(en) shape
die Forschung research
die Fortbildung further education
der Fortschritt(e) progress
das Foto(s) photo
der Foto(s) camera
der Fotograf(en)[1] photographer
die Frage(n) question; *das kommt nicht in Frage!* no way!
fragen to ask
Frankreich [n] France
französisch French
Frau Mrs, OR Ms
die Frau(en) woman, OR wife
Fräulein Miss
frech cheeky
die Frechheit(en) cheek, OR impudence; *so eine Frechheit!* what a nerve!
frei free; *im Freien* in the open air
Freitag [m] Friday
die Freizeit spare time
das Fremdenverkehrsamt("er) tourist office
fressen (animals) to eat, OR (slang) to scoff
sich freuen to be happy; *sich freuen auf* to look forward to
der Freund(e) friend, OR boyfriend
die Freundin(nen) friend, OR girlfriend
freundlich friendly
der Frieden peace
der Friedhof("e) cemetery
friedlich peaceful

frieren to freeze
das Frisbee(s) frisbee
frisch fresh
der Friseur(e)[2] hairdresser
die Frisur(en) hairstyle
früh early
der Frühling spring (season)
das Frühstück(e) breakfast
frühstücken to have breakfast
fühlen to feel
der Führer(-)[1] guide, OR guide book
der Führerschein(e) driving licence
füllen to fill
das Fundbüro(s) lost property (office)
funktionieren to work
für for
furchtbar awful, OR horrible
der Fuß("e) foot
Fußball [m] (UK) football, (US) soccer
der Fußball football (the ball)
der Fußgänger(-)[1] pedestrian
der Fußgängerüberweg(e) pedestrian crossing
das Fußgelenk(e) ankle

die Gabel(n) fork
gähnen to yawn
die Galerie(n) gallery
der Gang("e) corridor, OR (meal) course, OR (car, bike) gear
die Gangschaltung gears
ganz all (whole), OR quite (totally), OR whole; *ganz allein* on your own; *ganz wild auf ... sein* to be crazy about; *den ganzen Tag* all day
die Garage(n) garage
die Garderobe(n) cloakroom
die Garnele(n) king prawn
der Garten(") garden
das Gas gas
der Gaskocher(-) camping stove
der Gast("e) guest
der Gastarbeiter(-)[1] guest worker
der Gastgeber(-)[1] host
das Gebäude(-) building
geben to give
das Gebiß (PL: *Gebisse*) (riding) bit
gebraucht second-hand
gebrochen broken
das Geburtsdatum date of birth

der Geburtstag(e) birthday
das Gedicht(e) poem
die Geduld patience
gefährlich dangerous
gefallen to fancy (in German you say that "someone appeals to you") E.G. *Anna gefällt ihm* he fancies Anna
das Gefängnis(se) prison
das Gefühl(e) feeling
gegen against
die Gegend(en) area, OR neighbourhood
das Gegenteil(e) opposite
gegenüber opposite (facing)
gegrillt grilled
das Geheimnis(se) secret
gehen to go, OR to walk
geht: *wie geht es?* how are you?; *es geht* all right; *geht das?* is that possible?
die Geige(n) violin
geil* great, OR terrific
geizig stingy
gekocht boiled
das Gel(s) gel
gelaunt: *gut/schlecht gelaunt* in a good/bad mood
gelb yellow
das Geld money
der Geldautomat(en) cash dispenser
die Geldstrafe(n) fine
die Gelegenheit(en) opportunity
gemein nasty, OR rotten
gemischt mixed, OR co-ed
das Gemüse vegetables
genial brilliant (fantastic)
genug enough
geöffnet open
das Gepäck luggage
der Gepäckwagen(-) baggage trolley
gerade just (as in "just right"), OR straight (not curved)
geradeaus straight ahead
das Geräusch(e) sound
gerecht fair (just)
das Gericht(e) dish (meal)
gern (OR *gern haben*) to like, E.G. *ich hätte gern* I'd like, *ich schwimme gern* I like swimming
der Geruch("e) smell
das Gerücht(e) rumour
das Geschäft(e) shop
geschehen to happen
das Geschenk(e) present
die Geschichte(n) story, OR history
geschieden divorced

2: For a female the word is *die Friseuse(n)*.

das Geschlecht(er) sex (gender)

geschlossen closed, OR shut

der Geschmack("e) taste, OR flavour

die Geschwindigkeit(en) speed

die Geschwister [pl] brothers and sisters

geschwollen swollen

die Gesellschaft(en) society

das Gesicht(er) face

das Gespräch(e) conversation

der Gestank stink

das Gestell(e) (glasses) frame

gestern yesterday; *gestern abend* last night

gestreift striped

gestrichen cancelled

gesund healthy

die Gesundheit health

das Getränk(e) drink; *das alkoholfreie Getränk* soft drink

die Gewalt violence

das Gewicht(e) weight

gewinnen to win

das Gewitter(-) storm

die Gewohnheit(en) habit

gewöhnlich ordinary, OR usual

gewöhnt: *an ... gewöhnt sein* to be used to

das Gewürz(e) spice

gibt: *es gibt* there is/are

der Gips(e) plaster (cast)

die Gitarre(n) guitar

der Gitarrist(en)[1] guitarist

das Glas("er) glass; *ein Glas Wasser/Wein* a glass of water/wine

glatt smooth, OR slippery, OR (hair) straight

glauben to think, OR to believe

gleich equal, OR the same

gleichzeitig simultaneous

das Glück luck; *zum Glück* luckily

glücklich happy

glücklicherweise luckily

der Gott("er) god

der Grad degree

das Gramm(e) gram

das Gras("er) grass

die Gräte(n) fish bone

gratulieren to congratulate

grau grey

grausam cruel

die Grenze(n) border, OR frontier

der Griff(e) handle

die Grippe flu

grob coarse, OR rude, OR gross

groß big, OR tall, OR great

großartig terrific

Großbritannien [n] Britain

die Größe(n) size

die Großmutter(") grandmother

die Großstadt("e) city

der Großvater(") grandfather

großzügig generous

grün green

der Grund("e) reason

die Grundierung(en) (make-up) foundation

die Gruppe(n) group

gruslig scary

gucken* to look

gültig valid; *nicht mehr gültig* out of date

der Gummi(s)* condom

das Gummiband("er) rubber band

der Gummistiefel(-) wellington boots

günstig convenient, OR reasonably priced

die Gurke(n) cucumber

der Gurt(e) (riding) girth, OR (climbing) sling

der Gürtel(-) belt

die Gürteltasche(n) bum bag

gut good, OR well, OR fine (OK)

gutaussehend good-looking

das Gymnasium (PL: Gymnasien) secondary/high school

das Haar(e) hair

die Haarbürste(n) hairbrush

die Haarspange(n) (UK) hair-slide, OR (US) barrette

der Haarspray(s) hairspray

haben to have

das Hähnchen(-) chicken (for roasting, grilling)

halb half, OR (with time) half before, E.G. *halb elf* half past ten (half before 11)

halbdurch medium(-cooked)

das Halbjahr(e) (school) term

die Hälfte(n) half

hallo* hello, OR hi

der Hals("e) neck

die Halskette(n) necklace

Halsschmerzen [pl] sore throat

das Halstuch("er) (neck) scarf

halt! stop!; *halt den Mund!** shut up!

halten to hold, OR to keep, OR to stop

der Hamburger(-) hamburger

das Hammelfleisch mutton

der Hammer(") hammer

die Hand("e) hand

handgearbeitet handmade

das Handgepäck hand-luggage

die Handlung(en) plot

der Handschuh(e) glove

das Handtuch("er) towel

die Hängematte(n) hammock

hart hard

die Haselnuß (PL: Haselnüsse) hazelnut

hassen to hate

häßlich ugly

häufig common, OR frequent

das Hauptsegel(-) main sail

die Hauptstadt("e) capital city

das Haus("er) house; *zu Hause* at home

die Hausaufgaben [pl] homework

die Haut skin

das Heimspiel(e) home game

heiß hot

heißen to be called; *wie heißen Sie?*[2], OR *wie heißt du/ihr?*[2] what's your name?

der Heizkörper(-) radiator

die Heizung heating

helfen to help

hell bright, OR light

der Helm(e) helmet

das Hemd(en) shirt

herabgesetzt reduced

heraus'finden to find out

der Herbst autumn

herein'fallen auf to fall for (a trick)

herein'kommen to come in

der Hering(e) herring, OR (camping) tent peg

Herr Mr, OR gentleman

Herren gents

sich herum'treiben to hang around/out

das Herz(en) heart

herzlich warm; *herzliche*

1: For a female the word has *in* on the end (*innen* in the plural). **2**: *Sie* is the polite form for you, *du* and *ihr* are informal. For more about this see p. 44.

Glückwünsche congratulations; *herzlichen Glückwunsch zum Geburtstag* happy birthday; *herzliche Grüße* best wishes
heuchlerisch hypocritical
Heuschnupfen [m] hayfever
heute today; *heute morgen/abend* this morning/evening
hier here; *die hier** these; *der/die/das hier* this one
die Hilfe help, OR aid
die Himbeere(n) raspberry
der Himmel(-) sky
hin there; *hin und zurück* return (there and back)
hinauf'steigen to go/walk up
der Hindu(s) Hindu
sich hin'setzen to sit down
hin'stellen to put (down)
hinten behind, OR at the back
der Hintern(-)* bottom (bum)
hinunter'gehen to go/walk down
hinzu'fügen to add
hoch high
hochnäsig snooty
hoffen to hope
höflich polite
die höhere Bildung higher education
die Höhle(n) cave
die Höhlenforschung caving
holen to fetch
Holland [n] Holland
Holländer(-)[1] Dutch (man)
holländisch Dutch
die Hölle hell
das Holz(¨er) wood
der Holzhammer(¨) mallet
der Honig honey
hören to hear
der Hörer(-) (phone) receiver
das Horn(¨er) horn
das Horoskop(e) horoscope
die Hose(n) trousers
das Hotel(s) hotel
das Hovercraft(s) hovercraft
hübsch pretty, OR nice
der Hubschrauber(-) helicopter
der Huf(e) hoof
der Hügel(-) hill
das Huhn(¨er) chicken (live or for boiling)
der Humor humour
der Hund(e) dog
Hunger [m] hunger; *Hunger haben* to be hungry

die Hupe(n) horn (of car)
husten to cough
der Hut(¨e) hat
hysterisch hysterical

ich I, OR me
die Idee(n) idea
der Idiot(en) idiot
illegal illegal
die Imbißstube(n) snack bar
immer always
die Impfung(en) vaccination
in in, OR to, OR (slang) trendy
inbegriffen inclusive
Indien [n] India
die Informatik computer studies
das Insekt(en) insect
das Insektenschutzmittel(-) insect repellent
die Insel(n) island
das Instrument(e) instrument
interessant interesting
sich interessieren für to be interested in
international international
das Interview(s) interview
der Ire(n)[2] Irish (man)
irgend~ any, E.G. *irgendwo* anywhere
irisch Irish
Irland [n] Ireland
irre crazy
Italien [n] Italy

ja yes
die Jacke(n) jacket
das Jahr(e) year
die Jahreszeit(en) season
das Jahrhundert(e) century
Januar [m] January
je each; *je nach* depending on
die Jeans [pl] jeans
der Jeansstoff(e) denim
jede (OR *jeder* OR *jedes*) each, OR everybody, OR anyone
jemand anyone, OR somebody; *jemand anders* somebody else
jetzt now
joggen to jog
der Joghurt(-) yogurt
jonglieren to juggle
jüdisch Jewish
Judo [n] judo
die Jugendherberge(n) youth hostel
der/die Jugendliche(n) young person
Juli [m] July

jung young
der Junge(n) boy
Jungfrau [f] (star sign) Virgo
Juni [m] June

die Kabine(n) (boat) cabin, OR changing-cubicle
der Kabinenlift(s) cable car
der Käfer(-) bug (insect), OR beetle (insect or VW car)
das Kaff(s)* dump (dull, awful town)
der Kaffee coffee; *Kaffee und Kuchen* afternoon snack of coffee and cake
der Kalender(-) calendar, OR business diary
kalorienarm low-calorie
kalt cold; *es ist kalt* it is cold; *kalte Füße kriegen* to have cold feet (about something)
die Kamera(s) camera
der Kamm(¨e) comb
kämpfen to fight
der Kanal(¨e) canal, OR (TV) channel
das Kanu(s) canoe; *Kanu fahren* to go canoeing
kapieren* to get the message (understand)
der Kapitän(e) captain
kaputt* broken, OR exhausted
sich kaputt'lachen* to be in fits (of laughter)
kaputt'machen* to break
der Karabiner(-) karabiner
der Karneval(e) carnival
die Karotte(n) carrot
die Karriere(n) career
die Karte(n) card, OR ticket, OR map, OR (restaurant) menu
das Kartenspiel(e) card game
das Kartentelefon(e) card phone
die Kartoffel(n) potato
der Kartoffelbrei mashed potato
das Kartoffelpüree mashed potato
der Käse cheese
der Käsekuchen(-) cheesecake
die Kasse(n) check-out (cash desk), OR ticket office
die Kassette(n) cassette, OR tape
der Kassettenrecorder(-) cassette player, OR tape recorder
die Katastrophe(n) disaster

3: For a female the word is *die Irin(nen)*.

der Kater(-) tomcat, OR (slang) hangover

die Kathedrale(n) cathedral

katholisch Catholic

die Katze(n) cat

kaufen to buy

das Kaufhaus(¨er) department store

das Kaugummi(s) chewing gum

die Kaution(en) deposit

Kegeln [n] bowling

die Kehle(n) throat

kein (OR keine) not, OR not a(n), OR no, OR nobody

der Keks(e) (UK) biscuit, (US) cookie

der Keller(-) cellar

der Kellner(-) waiter

die Kellnerin(nen) waitress

kennen to know

kennen lernen to meet, OR to get to know

das Kennzeichen(-) car registration number

der Kerl(e)* bloke, OR guy

der Kern(e) (UK) pip, (US) seed

Kern~ nuclear, E.G. die Kernkraft nuclear power

das Kerngehäuse(-) core

die Kerze(n) candle

die Kette(n) chain

das Keyboard(s) synthesizer

der Keyboarder(-) synthesizer player

das Kilo(-) kilo

der Kilometer(-) kilometre

das Kind(er) child

das Kino(s) (UK) cinema, (US) movies

der Kiosk(e) kiosk

die Kippe(n)* fag (cigarette)

die Kirche(n) church

die Kirmes(sen) funfair

die Kirsche(n) cherry

die Kiste(n) box, OR chest, OR (slang) old banger (car)

kitzeln to tickle

Klacks: das ist ein Klacks* it's a piece of cake

Klamotten* [pl] clothes

der Klang(¨e) sound

klappen* to work (go well)

die Klarinette(n) clarinet

klassisch classical

der Klatsch gossip

klatschen to gossip, OR to applaud

das Kleid(er) dress

die Kleider [pl] clothes, OR dresses

klein little, OR small

das Kleingeld change (money)

der Kletterer(-)¹ rock climber

das Klettern rock climbing

der Kletterschuh(e) climbing shoe

das Kletterseil(e) climbing rope

klimatisiert air-conditioned

klingeln to ring

das Klo(s)* loo

klug clever

der Klüver(-) jib

der Knast* prison

das Knie(-) knee

der Knoblauch garlic

der Knochen(-) bone

der Knopf(¨e) button

der Knoten(-) knot

der Knüller(-)* hit (success)

kochen to cook

koffeinfrei decaffeinated

der Koffer(-) suitcase

die Kohle(n)* dosh (money)

Kohlensäure: mit/ohne Kohlensäure fizzy/still

die Kokosnuß (PL: Kokosnüsse) coconut

komisch funny

kommen to come

der Kompaß (PL: Kompasse) compass

die Konditorei(en) cake shop

das Kondom(e) condom

die Konfitüre(n) jam

die Konkurrenz competition

können can (to be able to), OR to know

das Konsulat(e) consulate

die Kontaktlinse(n) contact lens

der Kontrolleur(e)² ticket collector

kontrollieren to check

konventionell straight, OR conventional

das Konzert(e) concert

der Kopf(¨e) head; Kopf hoch! cheer up!

der Kopfhörer(-) earphones

der Kopfsalat(e) lettuce

Kopfschmerzen [pl] headache

das Kopftuch(¨er) (head) scarf

kopieren to copy

der Korb(¨e) basket

der Korken(-) cork

der Korkenzieher(-) corkscrew

der Körper(-) body

koscher kosher

kosmopolitisch cosmopolitan

kosten to cost

köstlich delicious

das Kotelett(s) (meat) chop

die Krabbe(n) prawn (small)

der Krach noise

der Kragen(-) collar

der Kram* stuff, OR kit

der Krampf(¨e) cramp

krank ill, OR sick

das Krankenhaus(¨er) hospital

der Krankenpfleger(-) nurse (man)

die Krankenschwester(n) nurse (woman)

der Krankenwagen(-) ambulance

kratzen to scratch

Kraul [n] (swimming) crawl

kraus (hair) frizzy, OR (clothes) crinkly

der Krawall(e) riot

Krebs [m] (star sign) Cancer

die Kreditkarte(n) credit card

die Kreide(n) chalk

die Kreidetasche(n) (climbing) chalk bag

der Kreisverkehr(e) roundabout

das Kreuz(e) cross (sign)

der Kreuzschlitz-schraubenzieher(-) Phillips® screwdriver

die Kreuzung(en) crossroads

das Kreuzworträtsel(-) crossword

der Krieg(e) war

kriegen* to get

der Krimi(s)* thriller

die Krise(n) crisis

kritisieren to criticize

der Krug(¨e) jug

die Küche(n) kitchen

der Kuchen(-) cake

die Küchenrolle(n) kitchen paper

die Kuh(¨e) cow

der Kühler(-) (car) radiator

der Kühlschrank(¨e) fridge

die Kühltasche(n) (UK) cool box, (US) ice chest

der Kuli(s) (ball-point) pen

der Kult(e) cult

die Kultur culture

kulturell cultural

der Kummer trouble, OR grief

der Kumpel(-) mate, OR pal

die Kunst art

1: For a female the word is *die Kletterin(nen)*. **2**: For a female the word has *in* on the end (*innen* in the plural).

die Kunsthochschule(n)
art school
der Künstler(-)[2] artist
der Kurs(e) course (series of
lessons), OR exchange rate
die Kurve(n) bend
kurz short
kurzsichtig short-sighted
der Kuß (PL: *Küsse*) kiss
küssen to kiss
die Küste(n) coast

lächeln to smile
das Lächeln smile
lachen to laugh
lächerlich ridiculous
der Lachs(e) salmon
der Laden(˝) shop
das Lamm(˝er) lamb (animal)
das Lammfleisch lamb
(meat)
das Land(˝er) country, OR
land, OR (German) state
die Landkarte(n) map
die Landschaft(en)
scenery (countryside)
lang (OR *lange*) long, OR for a
long time
langsam slow, OR slowly
sich langweilen to be bored
langweilig boring
der Lärm noise
der Laser(-) laser
lassen to leave, OR to let
lässig casual
lästig annoying
die Latte(n) (sailing) batten
die Latzhose(n) dungarees
laufen to run, OR (slang) to
walk
launisch moody
lausig* lousy
laut loud
der Laut(e) sound
der Lautsprecher(-)
(loud)speaker
die Lawine(n) avalanche
leben to live
das Leben(-) life
der Lebensstil lifestyle
die Leber(n) liver
lecker delicious
das Leder(-) leather
ledig single (unmarried)
leer empty
legen to lay down, OR to put
lehren to teach
der Lehrer(-)[2] teacher, OR
instructor
leicht easy, OR light (not
heavy)

leid: *es tut mir leid* I'm sorry
leiden to suffer
leider unfortunately
leihen to lend; *sich ... leihen*
to borrow
die Leinwand (cinema/
movie) screen, OR (art) canvas
leise quiet (not loud)
das Lenkrad(˝er) steering
wheel
die Lenkstange(n)
handlebars
lernen to learn
lesen to read
letzte (*letzter*, OR *letztes*) last
(the last), OR the latest
die Leute [pl] people
das Licht(er) light
der Lidschatten(-) eye
shadow
der Lidstift(e) eyeliner
pencil
lieb dear, OR lovely (nice)
die Liebe love
lieben to love
lieber (in letter) dear, OR
prefer (doing something), E.G.
ich male lieber I prefer
painting
die Liebesgeschichte(n)
romance
das Liebesleben love-life
lieb haben to love
(someone)
Lieblings~ favourite, E.G.
mein Lieblingshut my
favourite hat
liebsten: *am liebsten* best
das Lied(er) song
der Liegestuhl(˝e) deck chair
der Liegewagen(-) couchette
der Lift(s) (UK) lift, (US)
elevator
die Linie(n) line, OR route
linke (OR *linken*) left(hand)
links on the left; *links herum*
inside out
linkshändig left-handed
die Lippe(n) lip
der Lippenkonturenstift(e)
lip liner
der Lippenstift(e) lipstick
der/das Liter(-) litre
das Loch(˝er) hole
locker* relaxed, OR laid-back
lockig curly
der Löffel(-) spoon
der Lohn(˝e) wage
sich lohnen to be
worthwhile
los! come on!, OR go!; *was ist*

(denn) los? what's the matter?;
was ist los? what's wrong?
los lachen to burst out
laughing
los lassen to let go
los werden to get rid of
Löwe [m] (star sign) Leo
die Luft air
die Luftmatratze(n) (UK)
Lilo®, (US) air mattress
Luftpost [f] airmail
die Luftpumpe(n) pump
die Lüge(n) lie (fib)
lügen to lie (fib)
der Lügner(-)[2] liar
die Lust pleasure, OR desire;
hast du Lust ...? do you fancy
(doing something)?
lustig funny, OR cheerful;
sich über (...) lustig machen
to laugh at, OR to make fun of

machen to do, OR to make
macho macho
macht: *macht nichts!* never
mind!, OR it doesn't matter
das Mädchen(-) girl
der Magen(-) stomach
die Mähne(n) mane
Mai [m] May
das Make-up make-up
der Make-up-Entferner
make-up remover
das Mal(e) time (occasion)
malen to paint
man you (as in "you can't tell")
manche some, OR certain
manchmal sometimes
die Mandel(n) almond
der Mann(˝er) man, OR
husband
das Mannequin(s) model
die Mannschaft(en) team
der Mantel(˝) coat
die Margarine margarine
die Mark(-) mark (German
currency)
der Markt(˝e) market
die Marmelade(n) jam
März [m] March
die Maschine(n) machine
die Maske(n) mask
massenhaft loads of
der Mast(en) mast
Mathe* [f] maths
die Mayonnaise mayonnaise
meckern* to moan
die Medien [pl] media
das Medikament(e)
medicine (medication)
die Medizin medicine (science)

das Meer(e) sea
Meeresfrüchte [pl] seafood
mehr more
mein (or *meine*) my
meinen to reckon
die Meinung(en) opinion; *meiner Meinung nach* in my opinion
die meisten most (the majority)
der Meister(-)[1] champion
die Meisterschaft(en) championship
die Melone(n) melon
die Menge amount; *eine Menge* a lot of
der Mensch(en) person
die Menschenrechte [pl] human rights
menschlich human
das Menü(s) set menu
das Messer(-) knife
der Meter(-) metre
die Methode(n) method
die Metzgerei(en) butcher's
mies* grotty
mieten to rent
das Mikro(s)* microphone
die Mikrowelle(n) microwave
die Milch milk
der Milchshake(s) milk shake
minderjährig under age
das Mineralwasser mineral water; *mit Kohlensäure* sparkling; *ohne Kohlensäure* still
die Minute(n) minute
mit with
mit'bekommen to understand
das Mitglied(er) member; *Mitglied werden* to join
mit'machen to join in
mit'nehmen to take
Mittag [m] midday; *zu Mittag essen* to have lunch
das Mittagessen lunch
die Mitte(n) middle
mittelgroß medium (size)
mittelmäßig average
Mitternacht [f] midnight
Mittwoch [m] Wednesday
möchte: ich möchte I'd like
die Mode(n) fashion
das Model(s) model
modisch fashionable
das Mofa(s) moped
mogeln* to cheat
mögen to like

möglich possible
die Mohrrübe(n) carrot
Mokka~ coffee flavoured
der Moment(e) moment; *Moment mal!* just a moment!
momentan at the moment
der Monat(e) month
der Mond(e) moon
der Monoski(s) monoski
Montag [m] Monday
das Monument(e) monument
Moos* [n] dosh (money)
das Moped(s) moped
der Mord(e) murder
der Mörder(-)[1] murderer
morgen tomorrow; *morgen früh* tomorrow morning
der Morgen(-) morning
morgens in the morning
die Moschee(n) mosque
moslemisch Muslim
das Motorrad(̈er) motorbike
die Mücke(n) midge , or mosquito
der Mückenstich(e) midge/mosquito bite
der Müll (UK) rubbish, (US) garbage
der Mülleimer(-) (UK) rubbish bin, (US) garbage can
der Müllplatz(̈e) (rubbish/garbage) dump
die Mülltonne(n) (UK) dustbin, (US) trash can
der Mund(̈er) mouth
die Münze(n) coin
das Münztelefon(e) coin phone
das Museum (PL: *Museen*) museum
die Musik music
der Musikautomat(en) jukebox
der Musiker(-)[1] musician
der Muskel(n) muscle
müssen must, or to have to
das Muster(-) pattern
die Mutter(̈) mother
die Mütze(n) cap

na well ...; *na und?* so what?
nach after, or to; *nach draußen* outside
der Nachbar(n)[1] neighbour
nachher afterwards
die Nachlösegebühr(en) excess fare
der Nachmittag(e) afternoon

der Nachname(n) surname
die Nachricht(en) message
die Nachrichten [pl] news
die Nachspielzeit injury time
nächste(n) nearest, or next
die Nacht(̈e) night
der Nachteil(e) disadvantage
der Nachtisch(e) dessert
nackt naked
die Nadel(n) needle
der Nagel(̈) nail
die Nähe proximity; *in der Nähe (von)* near, or close (to)
naiv naïve
der Name(n) name
die Nase(n) nose; *die Nase in alles hinein'stecken** to be nosy; *die Nase voll haben** to be fed up
naß wet
national national
die Natur nature
natürlich natural, or of course
das Naturschutzgebiet(e) nature reserve
die Naturwissenschaften [pl] natural science
neben next to
necken to tease
nehmen to take, or to get
nein no
Nepp: so ein Nepp!* it's a rip-off!
der Nerv(en) nerve
der Nervenkitzel(-) thrill
nervös nervous
nervtötend nerve-racking
nett kind, or nice
neu new; *das neue Jahr* New Year
neugierig curious, or nosy
neulich recently
Neuseeland [n] New Zealand
nicht not
nichtalkoholisch non-alcoholic
Nichtraucher non-smoking
nichts nothing
nie never
niedergeschlagen dejected; *sich niedergeschlagen fühlen* to be/feel down
niedrig low
niemand nobody
niesen to sneeze
nirgendwo nowhere
noch still (even now); *noch mal** again; *noch mehr* more (additional); *noch nicht* not yet
der Norden north

 56 **1**: For a female the word has *in* on the end (*innen* in the plural). **2**: One German pound = 500 grams (46 grams more than the English/American pound).

nördlich north
normal normal
der Notausgang(ˉe) emergency exit, OR fire exit
die Note(n) mark (at school)
der Notfall(ˉe) emergency
nötig necessary
das Notizheft(e) notebook
die Notrufnummer(n) emergency number
November [m] November
die Nudeln [pl] pasta
Null zero
die Nummer(n) number
nur only; *nur so tun* to pretend E.G. *er tut nur so* he's pretending
die Nuß (PL: *Nüsse*) nut
der Nußknacker(-) nutcracker
nützlich useful
nutzlos useless

obdachlos homeless
oben above (overhead), OR upstairs; *oben ohne* topless
oberflächlich superficial
obergeil* out of this world
das Oberteil(e) top
das Objektiv(e) (camera) lens
obligatorisch compulsory
die Oboe(n) oboe
das Obst fruit
der Obstsalat(e) fruit salad
obszön obscene
oder or
offen open
offensichtlich obvious
öffentlich public
offiziell official
öffnen to open
oft often
ohne without
ohnmächtig unconscious; *ohnmächtig werden* to faint
das Ohr(en) ear
Ohrenschmerzen [pl] earache
der Ohrring(e) earring
okay* OK
die Ökologie ecology
Oktober [m] October
das Öl(e) oil
die Olive(n) olive
die Oma(s) granny
das Omelett(s) omelette
der Opa(s) grandpa
die Oper(n) opera
der Optiker(-)[1] optician
optimistisch optimistic
orange orange (colour)

Ordnung: *in Ordnung* all right, OR OK; *in Ordnung bringen* to fix (mend)
organisieren to organize
der Ort(e) place
Orts~ local E.G. *Ortsgespräch* local call
der Osten east
Ostern [n] Easter
Österreich [n] Austria
Österreicher(-)[1] Austrian (man)
österreichisch Austrian
Osteuropa eastern Europe
out* old-fashioned

paar: *ein paar* a few
paddeln to go canoeing
der Palast(ˉe) palace
die Pampelmuse(n) grapefruit
die Panne(n) breakdown, OR slip up
das Papier paper
die Papiere [pl] (identity) papers
das Papiertaschentuch(ˉer) tissue
die Paprikaschote(n) pepper
die Paranuß (PL: *Paranüsse*) Brazil nut
parken to park
das Parkhaus(ˉer) (multi-storey) car park, (US) parking lot
der Parkplatz(ˉe) (UK) car park, (US) parking lot
die Partei(en) (political) party
die Partie(n) game
der Paß (PL: *Pässe*) passport
der Passagier(e) passenger
passé old-fashioned
passen to fit, OR to suit
passieren to happen
die Pastete(n) pie
die Pauschalreise(n) package tour
die Pause(n) interval, OR rest
Pech! bad luck!, OR too bad!
das Pedal(e) pedal
peinlich embarrassing
perfekt perfect
die Periode(n) period (menstruation)
die Persönlichkeit(en) personality
die Pfanne(n) pan
der Pfeffer pepper
das Pferd(e) horse
der Pfirsich(e) peach
die Pflanze(n) plant

das Pflaster(-) (UK) plaster, (US) Band-aid®
die Pflaume(n) plum
Pflicht~ compulsory
pflücken to pick (gather)
das Pfund(-) pound (UK money or German weight[2])
die Pfütze(n) puddle
die Phantasie imagination
phantastisch fantastic
die Phobie(n) phobia
der Pickel(-) spot (pimple)
das Picknick(s) picnic
das Pils(-) lager
der Pilz(e) field mushroom
Ping-pong* [n] table tennis
der Pinsel(-) paintbrush
die Pinzette(n) tweezers
die Pistazie(n) pistachio nut
die Piste(n) (skiing) run
das Plakat(e) poster
der Plan(ˉe) plan
Plastik~ plastic
platt flat, OR (slang) stunned
der Platten(-) puncture
der Platz(ˉe) place, OR space, OR (in town) square, OR seat, OR (sports) court
platzen to burst
plaudern to chat
pleite broke (no money)
plötzlich suddenly
der Po(s)* bum
Polen [n] Poland
die Politik politics
die Polizei police
der Polizist(en)[1] police officer
Pommes* (OR *Pommes frites*) (UK) chips, (US) French fries
das Portemonnaie(s) purse
die Posaune(n) trombone
die Post (UK) post, (US) mail, OR post office
das Postamt(ˉer) post office
die Postkarte(n) postcard
die Postleitzahl(en) post/area code
praktisch practical
das Präservativ(e) condom
der Preis(e) price, OR prize
privat private
die Probe(n) test, OR rehearsal
probieren to try, OR to taste
prost cheers
protestantisch Protestant
die Prüfung(en) exam
das Publikum audience
der Pullover(-) (OR *der Pulli(s)***) sweater
pünktlich on time

die Qualität quality
die Qualle(n) jellyfish
die Quantität quantity
Quatsch rubbish; *Quatsch reden** to talk rubbish
die Quelle(n) spring (water)
die Querflöte(n) flute

der Rabatt(e) discount
die Rache revenge
das Rad(¨er) bike, OR wheel
der Radfahrweg(e) cycle track
raffiniert cunning, OR sneaky
der Rahmen(-) frame
ran'gehen* to answer (the phone)
(sich) rasieren to shave
der Rasierer(-) razor
die Rasierklinge(n) razor blade
der Rasierschaum shaving foam
rassistisch racist
das Rasthaus(¨er) service station
der Rat advice
raten to guess
das Rathaus(¨er) town hall
das Rätsel(-) puzzle
rauchen to smoke; *Rauchen verboten* no smoking
Raucher smoking
das Rauschgift(e) drug
der Rechner(-) calculator, OR computer
die Rechnung(en) bill
das Recht law; *recht haben* to be right
rechte(n) right(hand)
rechts on the right
das Reformhaus(¨er) health food shop
die Regel(n) rule
regelmäßig regular
der Regen rain
der Regenbogen(´) rainbow
der Regenmantel(´) raincoat
der Regenschirm(e) umbrella
der Regentropfen(-) raindrop
die Regierung(en) government
die Region(en) region
der Regisseur(e)[1] (film) director, OR (theatre) producer
regnen to rain; *es regnet* it's raining
reiben to rub
reich rich

reichen to pass
reicht: *das reicht* that's enough
reif ripe, OR mature
der Reifen(-) tyre
der Reifendruck tyre pressure
die Reihenfolge order
rein pure, OR (slang for *herein*) inside
der Reinfall(¨e) failure
die Reinigungslösung(en) cleansing solution
der Reis rice
die Reise(n) journey
das Reisebüro(s) travel agency
der Reisebus(se) (UK) coach, (US) bus
reisen to travel
der/die Reisende(n) traveller, OR (train) passenger
der Reisepaß (PL: *Reisepässe*) passport
der Reisescheck(s) traveller's cheque
reißen to rip
der Reißverschluß (PL: *Reißverschlüsse*) zip
Reiten [n] riding
der Reiter(-)[1] rider
die Reithose(n) jodhpurs
die Reitjacke(n) riding jacket
die Reitkappe(n) riding hat
die Reitpeitsche(n) whip
der Reitstiefel(-) riding boot
die Reizung(en) irritation
reizvoll attractive
der Rekord(e) record
rennen to run
das Rennen(-) race
das Rennrad(¨er) racing bike
reparieren to repair
reserviert reserved
die Reservierung(en) reservation
der Rest(e) rest (remainder)
das Restaurant(s) restaurant
retten to rescue
die Rettung(en) rescue
der Rettungsschwimmer(-)[1] lifeguard
die Rettungsweste(n) life jacket
der/das Revers(-) lapel
das Rezept(e) recipe, OR prescription
das R-Gespräch(e) (UK) reverse charge call, (US) collect call
richtig correct, OR right; *sich richtig aus'leben* to live it up

die Richtung(en) direction, OR way
riechen to smell
der Riemen(-) oar
das Rindfleisch beef
der Ring(e) ring
das Risiko (PL: *Risiken*) risk, OR chance
riskant risky, OR dodgy
riskieren to risk
der Rock(¨e) skirt, OR (music) rock
roh raw
Rollschuhlaufen [n] roller skating
der Rollstuhl(¨e) wheelchair
die Rolltreppe(n) escalator
der Roman(e) novel
romantisch romantic
rosa pink
der Rosé(s) rosé wine
rot red
der Rotwein(e) red wine
das Rouge blusher
die Route(n) route
der Rücken(-) back
Rückenschmerzen [pl] backache
Rückenschwimmen [n] backstroke
die Rückfahrt(en) return journey
rück mal! move over!
der Rucksack(¨e) backpack
rückwärts: *rückwärts fahren* to reverse (car)
das Ruder(-) rudder
das Ruderboot(e) rowing boat
rudern to row
die Ruderpinne(n) tiller
rufen to call, OR to shout
die Ruhe silence
ruhig calm, OR quiet
das Rührei(er) scrambled egg
der Rummel funfair, OR (slang) fuss
rund round
die Runde(n) round (of drinks)
der Rundfunk radio broadcasting
Rußland [n] Russia

die Sache(n) thing, OR matter
der Safe(s) safe (for valuables)
der Saft(¨e) juice
sagen to say, OR to tell
sagenhaft terrific
die Sahne cream
die Salami(s) salami

1: For a female the word has *in* on the end (*innen* in the plural).

der Salat(e) salad, OR lettuce
die Salbe(n) ointment
das Salz salt
salzig salty
sammeln to collect
Samstag [m] Saturday
der Sand sand
der Sänger(-)[1] singer
die Sanitär-Anlagen [pl]
washrooms (and toilets)
sarkastisch sarcastic
satt full
der Sattel(") saddle
die Satteldecke(n) saddle
cloth
sauber clean
sauer sour, OR (slang) cross
Sauerkraut [n] pickled
cabbage
die Sauerstofflasche(n)
oxygen bottle
saufen* to drink, OR to booze
das Saxophon(e) saxophone
der Saxophonist(en)[1]
saxophonist
Schach [n] chess
schade! what a shame/pity!
schaffen to manage, OR to
succeed
der Schal(s) scarf
die Schale(n) (apple) skin,
OR (egg) shell
die Schallplatte(n) record
sich schämen to be ashamed
scharf hot (spicy), OR sharp
(pointed)
der Schatten shade
schauen to look
das Schaufenster(-) shop
window
der Schaumfestiger(-)
mousse
das Schauspiel(e) play
der Schauspieler(-)[1] actor
der Scheck(s) cheque
das Scheckbuch("er)
cheque-book
die Scheibe(n) slice
der Scheibenwischer(-)
windscreen wiper
der Schein(e) note (money)
scheinen to shine, OR to seem
schenken to give
die Schere(n) scissors
schick smart (elegant)
schicken to send
schieben to push
der Schiedsrichter(-)[1]
referee, OR umpire
schießen to score (a goal);
zum Schießen sein* to be a riot

das Schiff(e) ship
das Schild(er) (road) sign
das Schimpfwort("er)
swearword
der Schinken(-) ham;
gekochter Schinken boiled ham;
roher Schinken smoked ham
schlafen to sleep
der Schlafsack("e) sleeping
bag
das Schlafzimmer(-)
bedroom
schlagen to hit, OR (sport) to
beat
der Schläger(-) thug, OR
(sport) bat, OR racket
die Schlägerei(en) fight
der Schlägertyp(en) thug
die Schlagsahne whipped
cream
Schlagzeug [n] drums
der Schlagzeuger(-)[1]
drummer
der Schlamper(-)*[1] slob
schlampig scruffy, OR sloppy
die Schlange(n) snake, OR
queue
schlank slim (thin)
schlau clever (crafty)
schlecht bad, OR badly
der Schlepplift(s) drag lift
schließen to close, OR to lock
schlimm bad, OR badly
die Schlinge(n) sling
der Schlitten(-) toboggan
der Schlittschuh(e) skate
das Schloß (PL: *Schlösser*)
castle, OR lock
Schluckauf [m] hiccups
schlucken to swallow
der Schluß (PL: *Schlüsse*) end
der Schlüssel(-) key
schmecken to taste
schmeißen to chuck (throw)
Schmerzen [pl] pain, OR ache;
Schmerzen haben to ache
die Schmerztablette(n)
painkiller
(sich) schminken to put on
make-up
der Schmuck jewellery
schmutzig dirty
die Schnalle(n) buckle
der Schnee snow
schneiden to cut
schneit: *es schneit* it's
snowing
schnell fast, OR quick
der Schnorchel(-) snorkel
die Schnur("e) string
die Schokolade chocolate;

die heiße Schokolade hot
chocolate
schon already
schön beautiful, OR (weather)
good; *schön kalt* nice and cold
Schotte(n)[2] Scottish (man)
schottisch Scottish
Schottland [n] Scotland
der Schrank("e) cupboard
die Schraube(n) screw
der Schraubenschlüssel(-)
(UK) spanner, (US) wrench
der Schraubenzieher(-)
screwdriver
schrecklich terrible
schreiben to write
der Schreibtisch(e) desk
schreien to shout
der Schriftsteller(-)[1] writer
schüchtern shy
schuften* to work
der Schuh(e) shoe
schuldig guilty
die Schule(n) school
die Schulter(n) shoulder
schulterlang (hair)
shoulder-length
das Schulterpolster(-)
shoulder pad
die Schüssel(n) bowl, OR dish
Schütze [m] (star sign)
Sagittarius
schwach weak; *mir ist*
schwach I feel faint
schwafeln to waffle
schwanger pregnant
der Schwanz("e) tail
schwänzen to bunk off
schwärmen (für) to
enthuse (about); *ich*
schwärme für ihn/sie I've got
a crush on him/her
schwarz black
schwätzen to natter
schweigen to be silent
das Schwein(e) pig
das Schweinefleisch pork
die Schweinerei* mess, OR
dirty trick; *Schweinerei!*
disgusting!
der Schweiß sweat
die Schweiz Switzerland
schwer heavy, OR hard
(difficult), OR serious
die Schwester(n) sister
schwierig difficult
das Schwimmbad("er)
swimming pool
schwimmen to swim
der Schwimmflügel(-)
(swimming) armband

2: For a female the word is *die Schottin(nen)*.

der Schwimmreifen(-) (swimming) rubber ring
die Schwimmweste(n) lifejacket
die Schwindelei(en)* fib
schwindlig dizzy
schwitzen to sweat
schwören to swear
der See(n) lake
die See sea
seekrank seasick
das Segelboot(e) sailing boat
segeln to go sailing
sehen to see
sehr very, OR a lot
die Seife(n) soap
das Seil(e) rope
sein to be, OR (OR *seine*) his
seit for, OR since
die Seite(n) page, OR side
die Sekunde(n) second
die Selbstbedienung self-service
selten rare (uncommon)
seltsam strange, OR weird
das Semester(-) six-month university term
der Sender(-) radio station
die Sendung(en) TV/radio programme
der Senf(e) mustard
September [m] September
die Serie(n) series, OR soap opera
die Serviette(n) napkin
der Sessellift(s) chairlift
der Sex* sex (intercourse)
sexistisch sexist
sicher sure, OR safe
die Sicherheit safety
der Sicherheitsgurt(e) safety belt
die Sicherheitsnadel(n) safety pin
sie her, OR she, OR them, OR they, OR (slang) it
Sie you (polite)
der/die Sikh(s) Sikh
Silvester [n] New Year's Eve
singen to sing
der Sinn(e) sense
sitzen to sit (to be sitting down)
der Sitzgurt(e) harness
der Ski(s) ski
der Skianzug("e) ski suit
die Skihose(n) ski pants
Skilaufen [n] skiing, OR to ski
der Skiort(e) ski resort
der Skipass("e) ski pass
der Skistiefel(-) ski boot

Skorpion [m] (star sign) Scorpio
der Slip(s) knickers
das Snowboard(s) snowboard
so so, OR like this/that; *(genau) so ... wie* (just) as ... as
die Socke(n) sock
sofort immediately, OR straight away
der Soldat(en)[1] soldier
sollen to be supposed to
der Sommer(-) summer
Sonnabend [m] Saturday
die Sonne sun
sich sonnen to sunbathe
die Sonnenblende(n) lens hood
der Sonnenblock(s) sun block
die Sonnenbrille(n) sunglasses
die Sonnencreme(s) sun cream
der Sonnenhut("e) sun hat
die Sonnenliege(n) (UK) sun lounger, (US) lounge chair
der Sonnenschirm(e) parasol
das Sonnenschutzmittel(-) sun cream/lotion
der Sonnenstich(e) sunstroke
der Sonnenuntergang("e) sunset
sonnenverbrannt sunburned
sonnig sunny
Sonntag [m] Sunday
sonst else, OR otherwise *sonst noch etwas?* anything else?
die Sorge(n) worry; *keine Sorge!* not to worry!
die Sorte(n) sort, OR flavour
soso so-so (not great)
die Soße(n) sauce
Spanien [n] Spain
die Spannung suspense
sparen to save (money, energy)
der Spaß fun; *zum Spaß* for a joke; *Spaß machen* to be fun, OR to be joking
spät late (not early)
spazieren'gehen to go for a walk
der Spaziergang("e) walk
die Speisekarte(n) menu
der Speisewagen(-) restaurant car
die Spezialität(en) speciality
der Spiegel(-) mirror
das Spiegelei(er) fried egg

das Spiel(e) game, OR match
spielen to play, OR to act
der Spieler(-)[1] player
die Spielhalle(n) (amusement) arcade
der Spielstand score
der Spinat spinach
der Spinnaker(-) spinnaker
die Spinne(n) spider
spinnen* to be nuts (crazy)
der Spion(e)[1] spy
die Spitze(n) end, OR tip
der Spitzname(n) nickname
spontan spontaneous
sportlich sporty, OR athletic
die Sprache(n) language
die Sprechanlage(n) intercom
sprechen to speak, OR to talk
springen to jump, OR to dive
die Spritze(n) injection
der Sprudel mineral water; *süßer Sprudel* lemonade
das Sprungbrett(er) diving-board
spucken to spit
das Spülmittel(-) washing-up liquid
die Staatsangehörigkeit(en) nationality
die Stadt("e) town
die Stadtmitte town centre
der Stadtplan("e) map (of town)
der Stadtrand suburbs
stark strong
die Station(en) (underground) station, OR (hospital) ward
stattdessen instead
der Stau(s) tailback
stechen (insect) to bite, OR to sting
stecken to put (in pocket/bag)
der Stecker(-) (electric) plug
stehen to stand, OR to suit E.G. *es steht dir/Ihnen gut* it suits you
stehlen to steal
steif stiff
der Steigbügel(-) stirrup
steil steep
der Stein(e) stone
Steinbock [m] (star sign) Capricorn
steinreich* loaded (rich)
die Stelle(n) job, OR place; *eine freie Stelle* a vacancy
stellen to put; *eine Frage stellen* to ask a question; *lauter/leiser stellen* to turn up/down (volume)

1: For a female the word has *in* on the end (*innen* in the plural).

stempeln: *stempeln gehen* to be on the dole
sterben to die
die Stereoanlage(n) stereo
der Stern(e) star (in sky)
der Stich(e) insect bite
stickig stuffy
der Stiefel(-) boot
der Stiel(e) stalk
Stier [m] (star sign) Taurus
der Stift(e) pen
still silent
die Stimme(n) voice, OR vote
stimmt: *das stimmt* that's right
stinken to stink
das Stipendium (PL: *Stipendien*) grant
das Stirnband("er) headband
der Stock(-) floor (level)
der Stoff(e) material (cloth)
der Stollen(-) stud (on boot)
stolz proud
der Stöpsel(-) plug (for water)
stören to disturb
stoßen to push; *stoßen gegen* to bump into
die Stoßzeit(en) rush hour
der Strand("e) beach
die Straße(n) road, OR street
die Straßenbahn(en) tram
die Straßenkarte(n) road map
das Streichholz("er) match
der Streit(e) quarrel
sich streiten to have an argument, OR to quarrel
streng strict
der Strom electricity
der Strom("e) (large) river
die Strumpfhose(n) tights
das Stück(e) piece, OR bit, OR (theatre) play
studieren to study
die Stufe(n) step, OR level
der Stuhl("e) chair
die Stunde(n) hour, OR lesson
der Stundenplan("e) timetable (school)
stur stubborn
der Sturm("e) storm
suchen to look for
der Süden south
südlich south
das Super (UK) four-star petrol, (US) premium gas
die Suppe(n) soup

das Surfbrett(er) surf board, OR **windsurfer** (board)
surfen to surf
der Surfer(-)[1] surfer, OR windsurfer (person)
süß sweet
die Süßigkeit(en) (UK) sweet, (US) candy
sympathisch likeable
synchronisiert dubbed

der Tabakladen(") tobacconist's
die Tablette(n) pill
der Tag(e) day; *am vorigen Tag* the day before
die Tage [pl] period (menstruation)
das Tagebuch("er) diary
die Tageskarte(n) daily travel pass
die Taille(n) waist
der Tampon(s) tampon
die Tankstelle(n) (UK) petrol station, (US) gas station
tanzen to dance
der Tänzer(-)[1] dancer
tapfer brave
die Tasche(n) bag, OR pocket
das Taschenbuch("er) paperback (book)
die Taschenlampe(n) (UK) torch, (US) pocket lamp
das Taschenmesser(-) penknife
die Tasse(n) cup
taub deaf
Tauchen [n] diving
der Taucher(-)[1] diver
der Taucheranzug("e) wetsuit
die Tauchermaske(n) (diving) mask
tauschen to swap
sich tauschen to be mistaken
der Tee tea (drink)
der Teil(e) part
das Teil(e) spare part
teilen to share
das Telefon(e) phone
das Telefongespräch(e) telephone call
telefonieren to phone
die Telefonkarte(n) phone card
die Telefonzelle(n) phone booth
der Teller(-) plate
das Tempo speed
der Termin(e) appointment (with doctor, lawyer), OR **deadline**

der Terminkalender(-) diary
teuer expensive
die Textverarbeitung word processing
das Theater(-) theatre; *Theater machen** to make a fuss
das Theaterstück(e) (theatre) play
die Theke(n) bar, OR counter
das Thema (PL: *Themen*) subject
das Thermometer(-) thermometer
die Thermosflasche(n) Thermos® flask
der Thunfisch(e) tuna
tief deep
das Tier(e) animal
der Tisch(e) table
Tischfußball [m] table football
Tischtennis [n] table tennis
todunglücklich heart-broken
die Toilette(n) toilet
toll* stunning, OR amazing, OR brilliant
die Tomate(n) tomato
der Ton("e) sound
der Topf("e) saucepan
das Tor(e) gate, OR goal
der Tormann("er) goalkeeper
das Törtchen(-) small tart
die Torte(n) tart, OR gâteau
tot dead
töten to kill
die Tournee(n) (music) tour
tragen to carry, OR to wear
der Trainingsanzug("e) tracksuit
die Trainingsschuhe [pl] (UK) trainers, (US) athletic shoes
trampen to hitch (a ride)
der Tramper(-)[1] hitch-hiker
die Träne(n) tear (in eye)
die Traube(n) grape
der Traum("e) dream
traurig sad
treffen to meet, OR to hit
trennen to separate
die Treppe(n) stairs
treu faithful
der Trickfilm(e) cartoon (film)
das Trikot(s) team shirt
trinken to drink
die Trinkflasche(n) water bottle
das Trinkgeld(er) tip (money)
der Tritt(e) kick
trocken dry

trocknen to dry
der Trödel(-) junk
die Trompete(n) trumpet
tschau* bye
die Tschechische Republik
Czech Republic
tschüs* bye
tun to do, OR (slang) to put
die Tür(en) door
der Türke(n)[1] Turkish (man)
die Türkei Turkey
turnen to do gym
die Turnhalle(n)
gymnasium
die Tüte(n) bag
der Typ(en)* bloke, OR guy
typisch typical

die U-Bahn underground
(trains)
üben to practise
über over, OR above
überall everywhere
die Überfahrt(en) (sea,
river) **crossing**
überfallen to attack
das Übergewicht excess
weight
überholen to overtake
übernachten to stay
(overnight)
überprüfen to check
überqueren to cross
die Überraschung(en)
surprise
überschätzt overrated
übersetzen to translate
übertreiben to exaggerate
übertrieben over the top,
OR (price) **excessive**
üblich usual
übrig spare
übrigens by the way
die Übung(en) exercise, OR
practice
die Uhr(en) watch, OR clock;
drei Uhr three o'clock; *elf
Uhr zwanzig* twenty past
eleven
um at, OR around
umarmen to hug
sich um drehen to turn
around/back
der Umkleideraum(¨e)
changing-room
die Umleitung(en) detour
um rühren to stir (cooking)
der Umschlag(¨e) envelope
sich um sehen to look
around (in shop etc.)
der Umweg(e) detour

die Umwelt environment
umweltfreundlich
environmentally friendly
der Umweltschaden(¨)
damage to the environment
der Umweltschutz
conservation
**die Umwelt-
verschmutzung** pollution
um ziehen to move house;
sich um ziehen to get changed
unabhängig independent
unangenehm unpleasant
und and; *und wenn* if
unentschieden draw
unerhört outrageous
der Unfall(¨e) accident
Ungarn [n] Hungary
ungefähr approximately
ungerecht unfair
ungewöhnlich unusual
das Ungeziefer creepy
crawlies
ungezwungen easy-going
unglaublich unbelievable
das Unglück(e) accident
unheimlich creepy, OR weird,
OR (slang) **really**, OR **very**
unhöflich rude
die Universität(en) (OR *die
Uni(s)**) university
die Unordnung mess
unrecht: *unrecht haben* to
be wrong (not right)
unschuldig innocent
unser (OR *unsere*) our
unter under
das Unterbewußtsein
subconscious
die Unterführung(en)
subway
sich unterhalten to chat
die Unterhose(n) underpants
die Unterkunft
accommodation
unterrichten to teach
die Unterschrift(en)
signature
der Untertitel(-) subtitle
die Unterwäsche
underwear
der Urlaub(e) holiday
ursprünglich original

der Vater(¨) father
die Verabredung(en)
appointment, OR date (with
boy/girlfriend)
verabscheuen to loathe
verantwortlich responsible
verärgert angry

der Verband(¨e) bandage
verblüffend stunning
verboten forbidden
verbrennen to burn, OR to
sting
verbringen to spend (time)
verdammt: *verdammt noch
mal!** damn!
verderben to spoil (ruin)
verdorben rotten (off)
der Verehrer(-)[2] admirer
der Verein(e) club
die Vereinigten Staaten
[pl] United States
sich verfahren to get lost
(in car)
vergessen to forget
die Vergewaltigung(en)
rape
verhindern to prevent
der Verkauf(¨e) sale
verkaufen to sell
der Verkehr traffic, OR
sexual intercourse
das Verkehrsamt(¨er)
tourist office
die Verkehrsstauung(en)
traffic jam
das Verkehrszeichen(-)
traffic sign
verkehrt wrong
verknallen: *sich in ...
verknallen** to fall for (a
person), OR to have a crush on
verlassen to leave
sich verlaufen to get lost
(on foot)
verlegen embarrassed
verleihen to lend
die Verletzung(en) injury
verliebt in love
verlieren to lose
vermieten to rent
vermischen to mix
vermissen to miss
vernünftig sensible
verpassen to miss
verrückt crazy, OR mad, OR
wacky, OR zany
verschieben to postpone
verschieden different
die Verschlußklappe(n)
lens cap
die Verschmutzung
pollution
verschwenden to waste
die Versicherung(en)
insurance
verspätet delayed
die Verspätung(en) delay
das Versprechen(-) promise

 62 **1**: For a female the word is *die Türkin(nen)*. **2**: For a female the word has *in* on the end (*innen* in the plural).

der Verstand common sense
die Verstauchung(en) sprain
verstecken to hide
verstehen to understand
verstopft blocked, OR constipated
versuchen to try
verteidigen to stand up for
vertrauen to trust
verwirren to confuse
verwöhnt spoiled (child)
verzeihen to forgive
Verzeihung sorry
die Videoanlage(n) video
viel much, OR a lot of
viele many
vielleicht perhaps
das Viertel(-) area (in town), OR quarter; *Viertel nach neun* a quarter past nine; *Viertel vor eins* a quarter to one
der Vogel(") bird
das Volksfest(e) funfair
voll full
völlig completely
das Vollkornbrot(e) who!emeal bread/loaf
die Vollwertkost wholefood
von of, OR by, OR from; *von wegen!** no way!
vor in front of, OR before, OR ago, OR (with time) **to**, E.G. *zehn vor acht* ten to eight
vorbei over (finished)
vorbei gehen an to pass
vorbei kommen to drop in
vor bereiten to prepare
Vorfahrt [f] right-of-way
das Vorhängeschloß (PL: *Vorhängeschlösser*) padlock
vorher beforehand
der Vormittag(e) morning
vorn (OR *vorne*) at/in the front; *von vorn* from the beginning
der Vorname(n) first name
vor lesen to read (aloud)
der Vorort(e) suburbs
vor schlagen to suggest
vorsichtig careful
die Vorspeise(n) first course
vor stellen to introduce (people); *sich vor stellen* to imagine (to picture a situation)
die Vorstellung(en) performance, OR idea
der Vorteil(e) advantage
vorübergehend temporary
die Vorwahl(en) (phone) code
vor ziehen to prefer

Waage [f] (star sign) **Libra**
wachsen to grow
wagen to dare
der Wagen(-) car, OR (train) (UK) **carriage**, (US) **car**
die Wahl choice, OR election
wählen to choose, OR to vote
wahnsinnig mad
wahr true
während while
die Wahrheit truth
wahrscheinlich likely, OR probably
der Wald("er) forest
Waliser(-)[2] Welsh
walisisch Welsh
die Walnuß (PL: *Walnüsse*) walnut
wandern to hike
die Wanderung(en) walk
wann when
warm warm; *es ist sehr warm* it is hot
die Warnung(en) warning
warten to wait
der Wartesaal (PL: *Wartesäle*) (station) waiting room
das Wartezimmer(-) (doctor's etc.) waiting room
warum why
was what, OR (slang) something; *was läuft?* what's on?
waschen to wash
die Waschmaschine(n) washing machine
das Waschpulver(-) washing powder
der Waschsalon(s) launderette
das Wasser water
wasserdicht waterproof
der Wasserfall("e) waterfall
der Wasserhahn("e) tap
der Wasserkanister(-) water bottle
Wassermann [m] (star sign) **Aquarius**
die Wassermelone(n) watermelon
Wasserskilaufen [n] water-skiing
die Watte cotton wool
der Wechselkurs(e) exchange rate
wechseln to change
die Wechselstube(n) foreign exchange office
der Wecker(-) alarm clock
weg away
der Weg(e) path, OR way
wegen because of

weg gehen to go away
weg laufen to run away
weg räumen to put away
der Wegweiser(-) signpost
weg werfen to throw away
weh tun to hurt
weich soft
Weihnachten [n] Christmas
weil because
der Wein(e) wine
der Weinberg(e) vineyard
weinen to cry (weep)
die Weinprobe(n) wine-tasting
die Weinrebe(n) vine
die Weinstube(n) wine bar
weiß white
der Weißwein(e) white wine
weit far
weiter machen to continue, OR to keep on (doing something)
welche (OR *welcher* OR *welches*) which
die Welle(n) wave
die Welt(en) world
der Weltraum (outer) space
wenig little
wenige few (not many)
wenn if, OR when
wer who
die Werbung(en) (cinema, TV) advertisement
werden to become
werfen to throw
die Werkstatt("en) garage, OR workshop
das Werkzeug(e) tool
der Werkzeugkasten(") tool box
die Wertsachen [pl] valuables
die Wespe(n) wasp
die Weste(n) waistcoat
der Westen west
der Wettbewerb(e) competition
das Wetter weather; *wie ist das Wetter?* what's the weather like?
die Wettervorhersage(n) weather forecast
wichtig important
Widder [m] (star sign) **Aries**
widerlich obnoxious
wie how, OR as (like); *wie bitte?* pardon? (what?); *wie geht's?* how are you?; *wie ist sie/er?* what's he/she like?; *wie oft?* how often?; *wie üblich* as usual
wieder again

wiederholen to repeat
Wiederhören (on the phone) goodbye
wieder sehen to see again; *auf Wiedersehen* goodbye
das Wiener Schnitzel(-) veal or pork escalope in breadcrumbs
wieviel? how much?, OR how many?; *wieviel Uhr ist es?* what time is it?
willkommen welcome
die Wimperntusche(n) mascara
windig windy
der Windschutz windbreak
die Windschutzscheibe(n) windscreen
der Winter winter
wir us, OR we
wirklich really, OR truly
die Wirtschaft(en) pub which serves food
wissen to know
die Wissenschaft(en) science
der Witz(e) joke
wo where
die Woche(n) week
das Wochenende(n) weekend
woher? where from?
wohin? where to?
wohl: *sich wohl fühlen* to feel well, OR to feel comfortable
der Wohltätigkeitsverein(e) charity organization
wohnen to live, OR to stay
das Wohnmobil(e) camper van
die Wohnung(en) (UK) flat, (US) apartment
der Wohnwagen(-) caravan
das Wohnzimmer(-) living room
die Wolke(n) cloud
die Wolle(n) wool
wollen to want
das Wort("er) word
das Wörterbuch("er) dictionary
worüber? what about?
worum: *worum geht es?* what's it about?
wozu? what for?
wunderbar wonderful
die Wundsalbe(n) antiseptic cream
der Wunsch("e) wish
wünschen to wish (hope for)

der Würfel(-) dice
wurscht: *das ist mir wurscht!* * I don't care!
die Wurst("e) sausage, OR cold meats such as ham, salami, pâté, etc.
das Würstchen(-) sausage
würzig spicy
der Wutanfall("e) fit, OR tantrum
wütend furious

zahlen to pay
zählen to count
der Zahn("e) tooth
der Zahnarzt("e) (OR *die Zahnärztin(nen)*) dentist
die Zahnbürste(n) toothbrush
die Zahnpasta toothpaste
Zahnschmerzen [pl] toothache
die Zange(n) pliers
der Zaum("e) bridle
das Zeichen(-) sign
zeichnen to draw
zeigen to show, OR to point at
die Zeit(en) time; *zur Zeit* at the moment
zeitgenössisch contemporary
die Zeitschrift(en) magazine
die Zeitung(en) newspaper
der Zeitungshändler(-) newsagent's
das Zelt(e) tent
zelten to camp
der Zeltplatz("e) campsite
das Zentrum (PL: *Zentren*) centre
zerreißen to rip (to shreds)
sich zerstreiten to fall out with (a person)
das Zeug stuff
ziehen to pull

ziemlich quite
die Zigarette(n) cigarette
das Zimmer(-) room
der Zirkus(se) circus
die Zitrone(n) lemon
der Zoll customs, OR toll
zollfrei duty-free
das Zoom(s) zoom lens
zu to (towards), OR closed, OR shut, OR too (too much)
der Zucker sugar
zuckerkrank diabetic
zuerst first, OR at first
der Zufall("e) chance, OR coincidence
zufällig by chance
der Zug("e) train
die Zügel [pl] reins
zu hören to listen
zu machen to close, OR to do up (fasten)
zu nehmen to put on weight, OR to increase (grow)
die Zunge(n) tongue
zurecht kommen to cope, OR to manage
zurück back
zurück kommen to come back
zurück rufen to phone back
zurück zahlen to pay back
zusammen together
zusätzlich extra (additional)
zu schauen to watch (look at)
der Zuschlag("e) supplement
das Zweibettzimmer(-) twin room
zweifelhaft dodgy
die Zwiebel(n) onion
der Zwilling(e) twin (brother/sister)
Zwillinge [pl] (star sign) Gemini
zwischen between
die Zwischenstation(en) stopover

First published in 1994 by Usborne Publishing Ltd, Usborne House, 83-85 Saffron Hill, London EC1N 8RT, England.

Copyright © 1994 Usborne Publishing Ltd.

UE. First published in America in March 1995.

Printed in Spain.